COMPLETE
MathSmart®

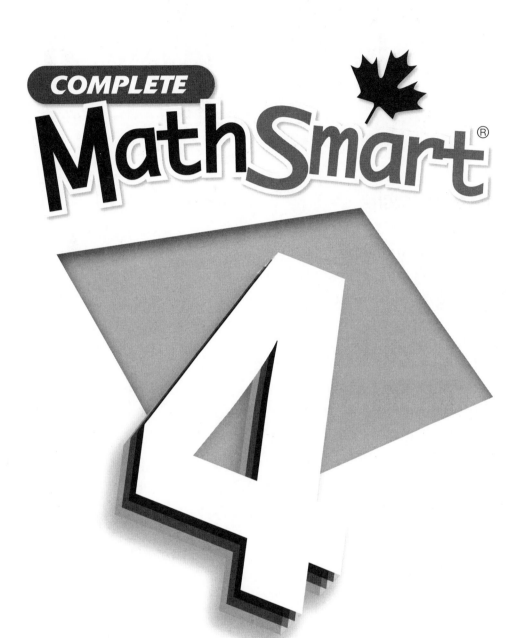

Contents

Level 1 – Basic Skills

Level 2 – Further Your Understanding

Level 3 – Applications

Dear Parent or Guardian,

Thank you for choosing our book to help sharpen your child's math skills. Our primary goal is to provide a learning experience that is both fun and rewarding. This aim has guided the development of the series in a few key ways.

Our *Complete MathSmart* series has been designed to help children achieve mathematical excellence. Each grade has 3 levels. In level 1, your child learns all the basic math concepts necessary for success in his or her grade. Key concepts are accompanied by helpful three-part introductions: "Read This" explains the concept, "Example" demonstrates the concept, and "Try It" lets your child put the concept to use. In level 2, and to a greater extent in level 3, these concepts are worked into relatable problem-solving questions. These offer a greater challenge and point children to the every-day usefulness of math skills.

Fun activities, lively illustrations, and real-world scenarios throughout the book help bring the concepts to life and engage your child. Additionally, the QR codes in the book link to motion graphics that explain key ideas in a fun and active way. After your child has completed the core content, they will find two assessment tests. These will test your child's general ability to apply the concepts learned, and prepare them for standardized testing. Finally, your child can use the answer key in the back of the book to improve by comparing his or her results and methods.

With the help of these features, we hope to provide an enriching learning experience for your child. We would love to hear your feedback, and encourage you to share any stories of how *Complete MathSmart* has helped your child improve his or her math skills and gain confidence in the classroom.

Your Partner in Education,
Popular Book Company (Canada) Limited

LEVEL 1
BASIC SKILLS

1 Numbers to 10 000

- reading, writing, and rounding numbers to 10 000

The value of each digit in a number depends on its position in the number.

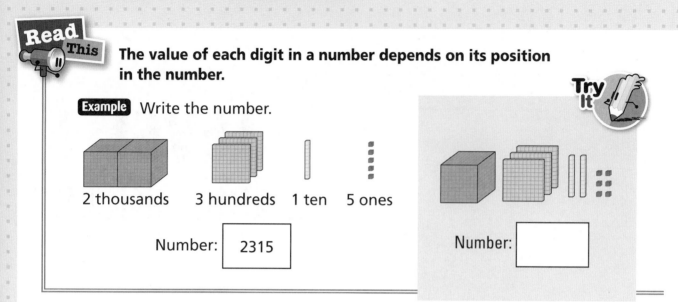

Example Write the number.

2 thousands   3 hundreds   1 ten   5 ones

Number: 2315

Try It

Number: ☐

Write the number shown by each group of base-ten blocks.

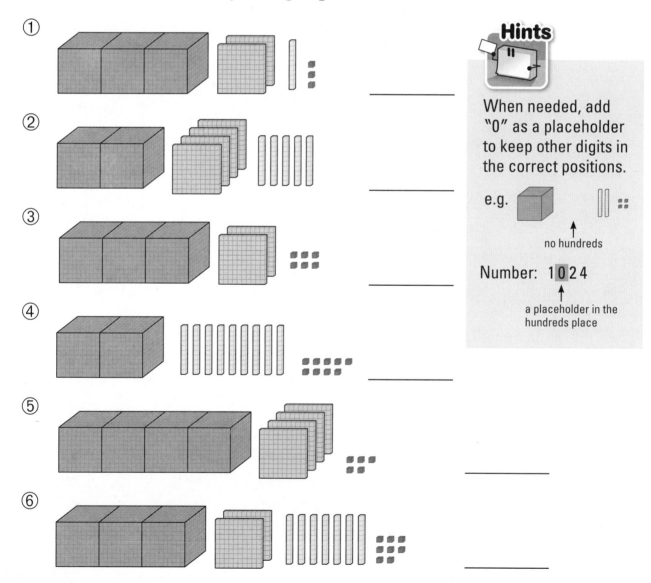

① _____

② _____

③ _____

④ _____

⑤ _____

⑥ _____

Hints

When needed, add "0" as a placeholder to keep other digits in the correct positions.

e.g.

↑ no hundreds

Number: 1 0 2 4

↑ a placeholder in the hundreds place

Match the groups of base-ten blocks with the numbers in the place value chart.
Write the letters.

⑦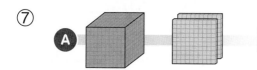

Thousands	Hundreds	Tens	Ones	
1	0	2	3	◯
	1	2	3	◯
1	2	0	3	◯

⑧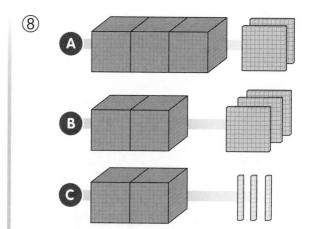

Thousands	Hundreds	Tens	Ones	
2	0	3	0	◯
3	2	0	0	◯
2	3	0	0	◯

Write the numbers in standard form, in expanded form, and in words.

⑨

Th	H	T	O
2	1	9	5

Standard form: _____

Expanded form: 2000 + _____ + _____ + _____

In words: two thousand one hundred _____

⑩

Th	H	T	O
4	0	9	7

Standard form: _____

Expanded form: _____

In words: _____

⑪

Th	H	T	O
1	4	8	0

Standard form: _____

Expanded form: _____

In words: _____

⑫

Th	H	T	O
2	8	0	9

Standard form: _____

Expanded form: _____

In words: _____

Write the value of each digit in bold.

⑬ **8**326 _____

⑭ **6**743 _____

⑮ 630**7** _____

⑯ **5**741 _____

⑰ 98**8**7 _____

⑱ 7**4**59 _____

⑲ 49**1**0 _____

⑳ 217**2** _____

㉑ 90**8**0 _____

㉒ 604**9** _____

㉓ 7**3**37 _____

㉔ **4**147 _____

Circle the numbers as specified.

㉕ **the smaller one**

   a. 1269

      1385

   b. 1649

      1684

㉖ **the greater one**

   a. 3021

      3124

   b. 5822

      5829

㉗ **the smallest one**

   a. 3024   4023   3204

   b. 5169   5619   5160

㉘ **the greatest one**

   a. 4832   4382   4328

   b. 6047   6470   6704

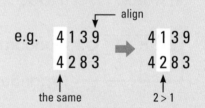

Hints

Comparing 4-digit numbers:

❶ Align the numbers to the right.

❷ Compare the digits in the thousands place. The number with a greater digit is greater. If they are the same, compare the digits in the hundreds place, and so on.

                   ┌── align

e.g.   4 1 3 9 ➡ 4 1 3 9

        4 2 8 3   4 2 8 3

        ↑   ↑

     the same   2 > 1

So, 4283 is greater than 4139.

Form the smallest and greatest 4-digit numbers using each set of digits.

㉙

  2 3

  0 1

_____ smallest

_____ greatest

㉚

  0 8

  9 0

_____ smallest

_____ greatest

Locate each number on the number lines. Then fill in the blanks.

 ㉛ **3870**

a.

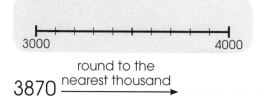

3870 $\xrightarrow[\text{nearest thousand}]{\text{round to the}}$ _____

b.

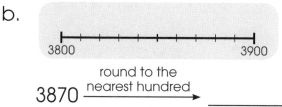

3870 $\xrightarrow[\text{nearest hundred}]{\text{round to the}}$ _____

c.

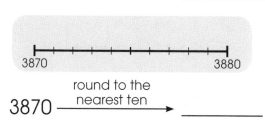

3870 $\xrightarrow[\text{nearest ten}]{\text{round to the}}$ _____

㉜ **5019**

a.

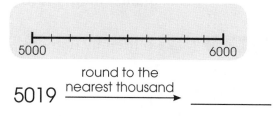

5019 $\xrightarrow[\text{nearest thousand}]{\text{round to the}}$ _____

b.

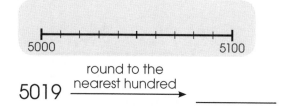

5019 $\xrightarrow[\text{nearest hundred}]{\text{round to the}}$ _____

c.

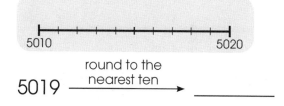

5019 $\xrightarrow[\text{nearest ten}]{\text{round to the}}$ _____

Round each number to the nearest ten, hundred, and thousand.

㉝

Round to the Nearest

	Ten	Hundred	Thousand
a. 7817	_____	_____	_____
b. 6018	_____	_____	_____
c. 8244	_____	_____	_____
d. 2455	_____	_____	_____
e. 8778	_____	_____	_____
f. 3419	_____	_____	_____
g. 1095	_____	_____	_____

 Hints

When rounding to the nearest 10, 100, or 1000, look at the ones, tens, or hundreds digit respectively. Round up if the digit is 5 or greater; round down if it is smaller than 5.

e.g. Round 2539 to the nearest
- ten:
  2539 $\xrightarrow{\text{round up}}$ 2540
  ↑
  9 > 5

- hundred:
  2539 $\xrightarrow{\text{round down}}$ 2500
  ↑
  3 < 5

- thousand:
  2539 $\xrightarrow{\text{round up}}$ 3000
  ↑
  = 5

2 Addition and Subtraction (1)

• using mental math to add and subtract 2-digit numbers

Read This

Friendly numbers, such as numbers that end in 0, make mental math much easier.

Example Make a friendly number. Then add.

$48 + 16 = ?$

Think Add 2 to 48 to make 50 (a friendly number). The 2 added to 48 is from the 16. Now there is only 14 more to add.

```
  + 2      + 14
 ⌢      ⌢
48  50        64
```

$48 + 16 = \boxed{64}$

Try It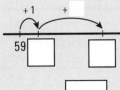

$59 + 23 = ?$

Think

Add 1 to 59 to make __?__ . The 1 is from 23. Now, there is only __?__ more to add.

```
   + 1    +
  ⌢    ⌢
59 □        □
```

$59 + 23 = \boxed{}$

Add the numbers using the friendly number strategy.

① $67 + 25 = $ _____

```
   +      +
  ⌢    ⌢
67 □        □
```

② $48 + 24 = $ _____

```
 +
48
```

③ $39 + 14 = $ _____

```
 +
39
```

④ $56 + 35 = $ _____

```
 +
56
```

⑤ $76 + 13 = $ _____

⑥ $49 + 37 = $ _____

⑦ $23 + 68 = $ _____

⑧ $15 + 69 = $ _____

Add the tens and ones separately to find the sums.

Hints

Another strategy for mental addition is to add the tens and ones separately and then regroup if needed to find the sum.

e.g. 57 + 16 = ?

		tens		ones
57	=	5 tens		7 ones
16	=	1 ten		6 ones
		6 tens		13 ones
regrouped →		7 tens		3 ones

So, 57 + 16 = 73.

⑨ 26 + 53 = _____

26 =   tens   ones

53 =   tens   ones
_____
     tens   ones

⑩ 45 + 32 = _____

45 =   tens   ones

32 =   tens   ones
_____
     tens   ones

⑪ 37 + 58 = _____

37 =   tens   ones

58 =   tens   ones
_____
     tens   ones

regroup →   tens   ones

⑫ 48 + 29 = _____

48 =   tens   ones

29 =   tens   ones
_____
     tens   ones

regroup →   tens   ones

Do the addition mentally using one of the two strategies mentioned.

⑬ 19 + 25 = _____

⑭ 16 + 74 = _____

⑮ 63 + 28 = _____

⑯ 35 + 16 = _____

⑰ 46 + 16 = _____

⑱ 73 + 19 = _____

⑲ 25 + 45 = _____

⑳ 64 + 18 = _____

㉑ 12 + 46 = _____

㉒ 12 + 21 = _____

㉓ 56 + 18 = _____

㉔ 13 + 32 = _____

㉕ 29 + 66 = _____

㉖ 44 + 18 = _____

㉗ 37 + 25 = _____

㉘ 36 + 41 = _____

Do the subtraction by counting forward on the number lines.

㉙ 58 − 24 = _____

Think Start with the smaller number (24) and then count forward to the bigger number (58).

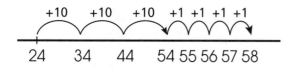

Add up the values of all the jumps: __34__

㉚ 70 − 46 = _____

Think Start with the smaller number (46) and then count forward to the bigger number (70).

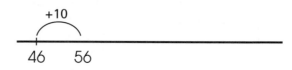

Add up the values of all the jumps: _____

㉛ 84 − 49 = _____

┼_____
49

㉜ 63 − 35 = _____

┼_____
35

㉝ 97 − 74 = _____

┼_____
74

㉞ 82 − 56 = _____

┼_____
56

Do the subtraction mentally.

㉟ 91 − 44 = _____   ㊱ 61 − 15 = _____   ㊲ 37 − 19 = _____

㊳ 50 − 21 = _____   ㊴ 43 − 16 = _____   ㊵ 64 − 37 = _____

㊶ 86 − 27 = _____   ㊷ 73 − 36 = _____   ㊸ 61 − 25 = _____

㊹ 47 − 19 = _____   ㊺ 32 − 14 = _____   ㊻ 57 − 28 = _____

㊼ 63 − 44 = _____   ㊽ 41 − 9 = _____   ㊾ 35 − 18 = _____

Make the second number friendly. Then do the subtraction.

(50) 74 – 49 = ______

Think

49 count 1 forward → ______

74 count 1 forward → ______

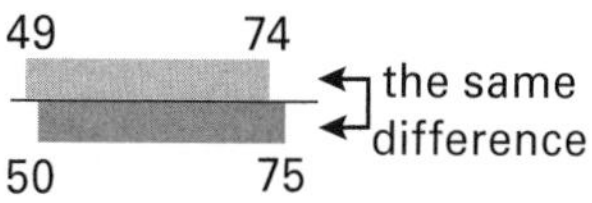

75 – 50 = ______

(51) 50 – 32 = ______

Think

32 count 2 backward → ______

50 count 2 backward → ______

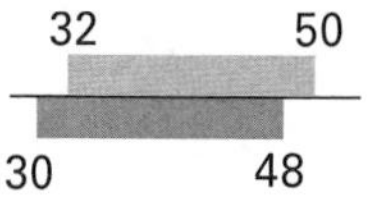

______ – ______ = ______

(52) 64 – 28 = ______

Think

28 count 2 forward → ______

64 count 2 forward → ______

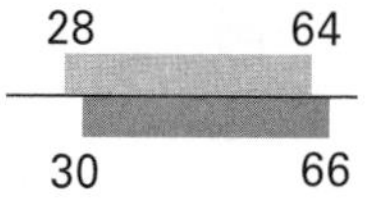

______ – ______ = ______

Subtraction is easier if the second number is a friendly number.

To make a friendly number, move both numbers in the subtraction sentence forward or backward together.

e.g. 51 – 22 = ?

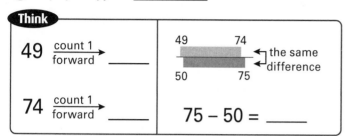

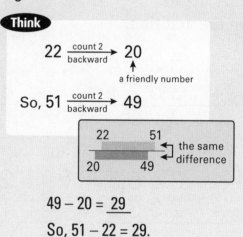

Think

22 count 2 backward → 20 (a friendly number)

So, 51 count 2 backward → 49

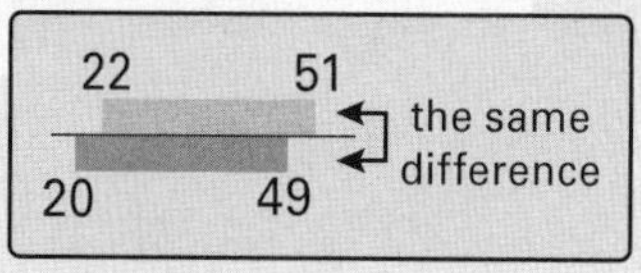

49 – 20 = 29

So, 51 – 22 = 29.

Do the subtraction mentally.

(53) 53 – 15 = ______

(54) 74 – 48 = ______

(55) 61 – 43 = ______

(56) 37 – 28 = ______

(57) 65 – 35 = ______

(58) 54 – 36 = ______

(59) 53 – 49 = ______

(60) 95 – 26 = ______

(61) 92 – 76 = ______

(62) 86 – 59 = ______

(63) 64 – 16 = ______

(64) 44 – 17 = ______

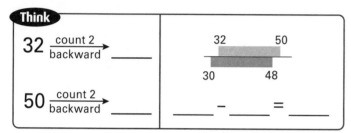

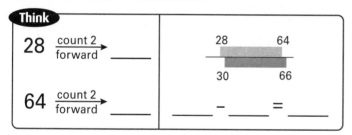

3 Addition and Subtraction (2)

• adding and subtracting 4-digit numbers

Read This

When adding and subtracting, align the numbers to the right and do the operation starting from the ones place.

Example 2605 + 4153 = ?

align

$$\begin{array}{r} 2\ 6\ 0\ 5 \\ +\ 4\ 1\ 5\ 3 \\ \hline 8 \end{array}$$ ⇒ $$\begin{array}{r} 2\ 6\ 0\ 5 \\ +\ 4\ 1\ 5\ 3 \\ \hline 5\ 8 \end{array}$$ ⇒ $$\begin{array}{r} 2\ 6\ 0\ 5 \\ +\ 4\ 1\ 5\ 3 \\ \hline 7\ 5\ 8 \end{array}$$ ⇒ $$\begin{array}{r} 2\ 6\ 0\ 5 \\ +\ 4\ 1\ 5\ 3 \\ \hline 6\ 7\ 5\ 8 \end{array}$$

2605 + 4153 = $\boxed{6758}$

Try It

$$\begin{array}{r} 4\ 7\ 4\ 2 \\ +\ \ \ 3\ 1\ 5\ 7 \\ \hline \end{array}$$

Do the addition.

① $$\begin{array}{r} 5\ 2\ 7\ 4 \\ +\ \ 3\ 5\ 2\ 1 \\ \hline \end{array}$$

② $$\begin{array}{r} 1\ 7\ 8\ 3 \\ +\ \ 8\ 2\ 1\ 4 \\ \hline \end{array}$$

③ $$\begin{array}{r} 3\ 6\ 5\ 3 \\ +\ \ 2\ 3\ 3\ 5 \\ \hline \end{array}$$

④ $$\begin{array}{r} 2\ 5\ 7\ 7 \\ +\ \ 1\ 7\ 1\ 8 \\ \hline \end{array}$$

⑤ $$\begin{array}{r} 4\ 2\ 1\ 8 \\ +\ \ 1\ 0\ 4\ 9 \\ \hline \end{array}$$

⑥ $$\begin{array}{r} 5\ 0\ 0\ 8 \\ +\ \ 1\ 7\ 9\ 4 \\ \hline \end{array}$$

Tips

Regroup when the numbers add up to 10 or more.

e.g.
$$\begin{array}{r} {}^{①}{}^{①} \\ 1\ 3\ 2\ 8 \\ +\ \ 2\ 1\ 7\ 4 \\ \hline 3\ 5\ 0\ 2 \end{array}$$

1 + 2 = 3 ⤴

8 + 4 = 12 (1 ten 2 ones)

1 + 3 + 1 = 5 ⤴

1 + 2 + 7 = 10 (1 hundred 0 tens)

⑦ 5050 + 3034 = _____

⑧ 8222 + 1686 = _____

⑨ 8202 + 1597 = _____

⑩ 1700 + 5443 = _____

⑪ 4199 + 4620 = _____

⑫ 2727 + 6937 = _____

⑬ 3971 + 5345 = _____

⑭ 4758 + 3012 = _____

⑮ 2781 + 3609 = _____

⑯ 2268 + 5324 = _____

Do the addition. Show your work.

⑰ a. 6705 + 848 = _____

    b. 1238 + 772 = _____

    c. 5987 + 605 = _____

    d. 2269 + 35 = _____

    e. 3895 + 79 = _____

    f. 1104 + 470 = _____

Tips

Make sure the numbers are aligned to the right before adding.

e.g.

    2 4 7 5
+ 3 0 9
✗

         align

    2 4 7 5
+   3 0 9
✓

$$+ \underline{\hspace{3cm}}$$

Find the answers.

⑱ 8155 + 103 = _____

⑲ 7396 + 225 = _____

⑳ 6836 + 23 = _____

㉑ 4763 + 29 = _____

㉒ 1458 + 304 = _____

㉓ 8568 + 78 = _____

㉔ 3555 + 215 = _____

㉕ 2078 + 92 = _____

㉖ 1979 + 79 = _____

㉗ 7328 + 578 = _____

㉘ 8255 + 486 = _____

㉙ 1899 + 754 = _____

Do the vertical subtraction.

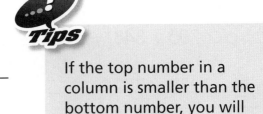

30)
```
   4 5 6 8
 - 1 3 4 1
```

31)
```
   6 6 5 9
 - 5 2 1 6
```

If the top number in a column is smaller than the bottom number, you will need to regroup.

32)
```
   4 7 8 9
 - 4 5 2 7
```

33)
```
   2 8 4 0
 - 1 0 7 3
```

e.g.
```
       9
   3  10  10
   4  0  0  9
 - 2  5  8  3
   1  4  2  6
```
$3 - 2 = 1$
$9 - 5 = 4$
$0 < 8$; since there are no hundreds, regroup 1 thousand as 10 hundreds. Then regroup 1 hundred as 10 tens, leaving 9 in the hundreds column; $10 - 8 = 2$.
$9 - 3 = 6$

34)
```
   6 3 8 8
 - 2 9 3 0
```

35)
```
   8 5 4 9
 - 3 7 6 7
```

36)
```
   9 3 0 7
 - 1 2 5 1
```

37)
```
   7 8 4 9
 - 1 2 8 5
```

Find the answers. Show your work.

38) a. 3195 – 719 = _____

   b. 1673 – 639 = _____

   c. 7103 – 188 = _____

   d. 6182 – 925 = _____

   e. 1004 – 244 = _____

   f. 8995 – 753 = _____

   g. 1208 – 386 = _____

   h. 5026 – 360 = _____

Find the sum and difference of each pair of numbers. Show your work.

㉟㊴ (39) **4319   2412**

Sum:

Difference:

(40) **3098   976**

Sum:

Difference:

Tips

Subtract the smaller number from the greater number to find the difference.

(41) **658   7164**

Sum:

Difference:

(42) **2156   293**

Sum:

Difference:

(43) **3218   6000**

Sum:

Difference:

Find the missing numbers.

(44)
```
  3 _ 45
+ _ 6 3
-------
  486
```

(45)
```
  408
+ _ 169
-------
  6 _ 54
```

Tips

Pay attention to the regrouped digits.

(46)
```
  219
- 148
-----
  17 _ 3
```

(47)
```
  60 _ 1
- _ 716
------
  3 _ 4
```

4 Multiplication Facts to 81

• multiplying 1-digit numbers by 1-digit numbers

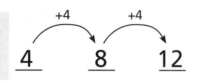

Read This

Skip counting can help you do multiplication.

Example 4 x 3 = ?

Skip count by 4's to find the first 3 numbers.

+4 +4

4 → 8 → 12

4 x 3 = 12

Try It

6 x 4 = ☐

Skip count by 6's to find the first 4 numbers.

6 → ☐ → ☐ → ☐

Find the answers by skip counting.

① 6 x 3 = ______

6 → ____ → ____

② 7 x 4 = ______

7 → ____ → ____ → ____

③ 5 x 6 = ______

④ 8 x 3 = ______

⑤ 4 x 5 = ______

⑥ 2 x 6 = ______

⑦ 8 x 8 = ______ 8 → ____ → ____ → ____ → ____ → ____ → ____ → ____

⑧ 9 x 7 = ______

⑨ 7 x 6 = ______

⑩ 6 x 9 = ______

Write two multiplication sentences for each group.

⑪

$$6 \times 3 = \underline{\hspace{2cm}}$$

$$2 \times 9 = \underline{\hspace{2cm}}$$

⑫

_____

_____

⑬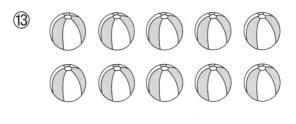

_____

_____

⑭

_____

_____

⑮

_____

_____

⑯

_____

_____

Do the multiplication using the times table.

1 x 1 = 1 1 x 2 = 2 1 x 3 = 3 1 x 4 = 4 1 x 5 = 5 1 x 6 = 6 1 x 7 = 7 1 x 8 = 8 1 x 9 = 9 1 x 10 = 10	2 x 1 = 2 2 x 2 = 4 2 x 3 = 6 2 x 4 = 8 2 x 5 = 10 2 x 6 = 12 2 x 7 = 14 2 x 8 = 16 2 x 9 = 18 2 x 10 = 20	3 x 1 = 3 3 x 2 = 6 3 x 3 = 9 3 x 4 = 12 3 x 5 = 15 3 x 6 = 18 3 x 7 = 21 3 x 8 = 24 3 x 9 = 27 3 x 10 = 30	4 x 1 = 4 4 x 2 = 8 4 x 3 = 12 4 x 4 = 16 4 x 5 = 20 4 x 6 = 24 4 x 7 = 28 4 x 8 = 32 4 x 9 = 36 4 x 10 = 40	5 x 1 = 5 5 x 2 = 10 5 x 3 = 15 5 x 4 = 20 5 x 5 = 25 5 x 6 = 30 5 x 7 = 35 5 x 8 = 40 5 x 9 = 45 5 x 10 = 50
6 x 1 = 6 6 x 2 = 12 6 x 3 = 18 6 x 4 = 24 6 x 5 = 30 6 x 6 = 36 6 x 7 = 42 6 x 8 = 48 6 x 9 = 54 6 x 10 = 60	7 x 1 = 7 7 x 2 = 14 7 x 3 = 21 7 x 4 = 28 7 x 5 = 35 7 x 6 = 42 7 x 7 = 49 7 x 8 = 56 7 x 9 = 63 7 x 10 = 70	8 x 1 = 8 8 x 2 = 16 8 x 3 = 24 8 x 4 = 32 8 x 5 = 40 8 x 6 = 48 8 x 7 = 56 8 x 8 = 64 8 x 9 = 72 8 x 10 = 80	9 x 1 = 9 9 x 2 = 18 9 x 3 = 27 9 x 4 = 36 9 x 5 = 45 9 x 6 = 54 9 x 7 = 63 9 x 8 = 72 9 x 9 = 81 9 x 10 = 90	10 x 1 = 10 10 x 2 = 20 10 x 3 = 30 10 x 4 = 40 10 x 5 = 50 10 x 6 = 60 10 x 7 = 70 10 x 8 = 80 10 x 9 = 90 10 x 10 = 100

⑰

a. 3 x 4 = _____

b. 5 x 2 = _____

c. 2 x 8 = _____

d. 7 x 3 = _____

e. 5 x 3 = _____

f. 9 x 2 = _____

g. 8 x 1 = _____

h. 4 x 5 = _____

i. 3 x 6 = _____

j. 7 x 4 = _____

k. 5 x 9 = _____

l. 8 x 7 = _____

m. 4 x 8 = _____

n. 6 x 9 = _____

o.
```
    2
x   4
_____
```

p.
```
    9
x   1
_____
```

q.
```
    5
x   5
_____
```

r.
```
    8
x   6
_____
```

Tips

Memorizing the times table will help make multiplication easier.

For each group, cross out the number sentence that does not belong.

⑱ (A) 7 x 6

(B) 7 + 6

(C) 6 sevens

(D) 7 groups of 6

⑲ (A) 5 threes

(B) 3 x 5

(C) 5 + 5 + 5 + 5 + 5

(D) 3 times 5

⑳ (A) 4 + 4 + 4 + 4

(B) 4 ones

(C) 1 x 4

(D) 1 group of 4

㉑ (A) 6 times 5

(B) 6 + 5 + 6 + 5 + 6

(C) 6 groups of 5

(D) 6 x 5

Complete the multiplication table.

㉒

X	1	2	3	4	5	6	7	8	9
1									
2	2								
3				12					
4									
5									
6							42		
7									
8		16							
9						54			

Each box contains the product of the row number and the column number.

36 — $\underset{\text{product}}{\underline{36}} = \underset{\substack{\text{row} \\ \text{number}}}{\underline{4}} \times \underset{\substack{\text{column} \\ \text{number}}}{\underline{9}}$

5 Multiplying 2-digit Numbers

- multiplying 2-digit numbers by 1-digit numbers

Read This

When multiplying 2-digit numbers by 1-digit numbers, first align the numbers to the right. Then multiply each digit of the number in the top row from right to left by the number in the bottom row.

Example 12 x 4 = ?

*Normally the smaller number goes in the bottom row.

```
    align
  1 2          1 2          1 2
x   4    →   x   4    →   x   4
               8            4 8
              ↑              ↑
             2 x 4          1 x 4
```

12 x 4 = ☐ 48

Try It

31 x 4 = ?

```
    3 1
x     4
  ☐
```

Do the multiplication.

①
```
  3 4
x   2
```

②
```
  1 1
x   6
```

Tips Remember to regroup if the multiplication results in a 2-digit number.

e.g.
```
     3
   1 4
x    8
 1 1 2
```

8 x 1 = 8; add the 3 to get 11.

8 x 4 = 32; regroup 32 as 3 tens and 2 ones.

③
```
  3 2
x   4
```

④
```
  4 2
x   3
```

⑤
```
  1 8
x   5
```

⑥
```
  2 6
x   7
```

⑦
```
  2 2
x   9
```

⑧
```
  4 5
x   5
```

⑨
```
  1 7
x   8
```

⑩
```
  6 8
x   2
```

Do the multiplication. Show your work.

⑪ 11 x 9 = _____

⑫ 35 x 3 = _____

⑬ 45 x 2 = _____

⑭ 29 x 6 = _____

⑮ 18 x 7 = _____

⑯ 27 x 4 = _____

⑰ 46 x 6 = _____

⑱ 19 x 5 = _____

⑲ 52 x 8 = _____

Do the multiplication. Then draw lines to connect the questions that have the same answer.

⑳

```
   1 8
×    6
_____
```
•

```
   2 4
×    4
_____
```
•

```
   7 8
×    2
_____
```
•

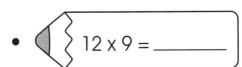

• 12 x 9 = _____

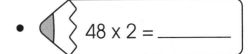

• 48 x 2 = _____

• 36 x 3 = _____

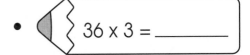

• 52 x 3 = _____

• 12 x 8 = _____

• 26 x 6 = _____

Do the multiplication. Then use the answers to decode and solve the riddle.

㉑   45 x 3 = _____ W

㉒   27 x 8 = _____ I

㉓   36 x 2 = _____ N

㉔   92 x 7 = _____ I

㉕   84 x 3 = _____ N

㉖   78 x 9 = _____ T

㉗   15 x 4 = _____ R

㉘   28 x 5 = _____ S

㉙   49 x 8 = _____ T

㉚   63 x 7 = _____ N

㉛   55 x 3 = _____ A

㉜   42 x 4 = _____ I

㉝   81 x 6 = _____ G

㉞   67 x 5 = _____ A

Do your work here.

Two friends and a dog were walking outside without umbrellas. Why didn't they get wet?

___	___		___	___	___	___	___ ,
216	392		135	165	140	72	702

___	___	___	___	___	___	___ !
60	335	644	441	168	252	486

For each group, write the correct multiplication sentence to find the total.

③⑤

_____ X _____ = _____

Total: _____

Hints

Changing the order of the numbers in a multiplication problem does not change the answer.

e.g.   12 x 5 = 60
        5 x 12 = 60
        12 x 5 = 5 x 12

③⑥

_____ X _____ = _____

Total: _____

③⑦

15
15
15
15
15

_____ X _____ = _____

Total: _____

③⑧ **A** $25 each **B**

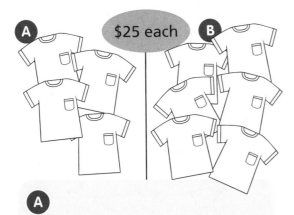

A

_____ X _____ = _____

Total: $_____

B

_____ X _____ = _____

Total: $_____

③⑨ **A**   18 m each **B**

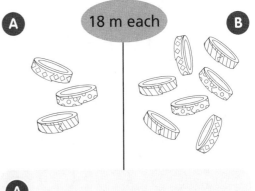

A

_____ X _____ = _____

Total: _____ m

B

_____ X _____ = _____

Total: _____ m

6 Division Facts to 81

- dividing numbers up to 81

Division is the process of splitting objects into equal groups.

Example Check the statements that describe the division sentence.

$6 \div 2$

☑ Put 6 into 2 groups.

◯ Put 2 into 6 groups.

☑ Put 6 into groups of 2.

Try It

$12 \div 4$

Ⓐ Put 12 into groups of 4.

Ⓑ Put 12 into 4 groups.

Ⓒ Put 4 into groups of 12.

Circle to divide the shapes into equal groups. Then write the answers.

①

Put 12 ♡ into 4 groups.

$12 \div 4 =$ _____

_____ ♡ in each group

Put 12 ♡ into groups of 4.

$12 \div 4 =$ _____

_____ equal groups

②

Put 10 ☆ into 2 groups.

$10 \div 2 =$ _____

_____ ☆ in each group

Put 10 ☆ into groups of 2.

$10 \div 2 =$ _____

_____ equal groups

Match each diagram with the correct multiplication sentence and write two related division sentences for it. Then answer the question.

③

A

B

C

D

E

F

○ 3 x 5 = 15

15 ÷ ____ = ____

15 ÷ ____ = ____

○ 7 x 3 = 21

21 ÷ ____ = ____

21 ÷ ____ = ____

○ 8 x 2 = 16

16 ÷ ____ = ____

16 ÷ ____ = ____

○ 6 x 4 = 24

24 ÷ ____ = ____

24 ÷ ____ = ____

○ 5 x 4 = 20

20 ÷ ____ = ____

20 ÷ ____ = ____

○ 3 x 6 = 18

18 ÷ ____ = ____

18 ÷ ____ = ____

④ How are multiplication and division related? Write two related division facts for 6 x 5 = 30. You may draw a diagram to support your answer.

_____

_____

_____

For each division problem, write a related multiplication fact. Then find the answer.

⑤ $42 \div 7 = \boxed{}$

$7 \times \underline{\hspace{1cm}} = 42$

⑥ $24 \div 3 = \boxed{}$

⑦ $30 \div 5 = \boxed{}$

⑧ $32 \div 4 = \boxed{}$

⑨ $48 \div 6 = \boxed{}$

⑩ $27 \div 9 = \boxed{}$

⑪ $35 \div 7 = \boxed{}$

⑫ $36 \div 6 = \boxed{}$

Hints

Familiarizing yourself with multiplication facts can help you do division.

e.g. $35 \div 7 = ?$

Think $7 \times ? = 35$

$7 \times 1 = 7$
$\vdots$
$7 \times 4 = 28$
$7 \times 5 = 35 \longleftarrow$ the related fact

So, $35 \div 7 = 5$.

Do the division and write the related division facts. Then write two new pairs of related division facts.

⑬ $42 \div 6 = \underline{\hspace{1.5cm}}$

$42 \div \underline{\hspace{1cm}} = 6$

⑭ $45 \div 9 = \underline{\hspace{1.5cm}}$

$\underline{\hspace{3cm}}$

⑮ $32 \div 8 = \underline{\hspace{1.5cm}}$

$\underline{\hspace{3cm}}$

⑯ $28 \div 7 = \underline{\hspace{1.5cm}}$

$\underline{\hspace{3cm}}$

⑰ $21 \div 3 = \underline{\hspace{1.5cm}}$

$\underline{\hspace{3cm}}$

⑱ $54 \div 6 = \underline{\hspace{1.5cm}}$

$\underline{\hspace{3cm}}$

⑲ $40 \div 5 = \underline{\hspace{1.5cm}}$

$\underline{\hspace{3cm}}$

⑳ $16 \div 8 = \underline{\hspace{1.5cm}}$

$\underline{\hspace{3cm}}$

㉑ $72 \div 9 = \underline{\hspace{1.5cm}}$

$\underline{\hspace{3cm}}$

㉒ **Division Facts**

$\underline{\hspace{3cm}}$

$\underline{\hspace{3cm}}$

$\underline{\hspace{3cm}}$

$\underline{\hspace{3cm}}$

Do the division. Then colour the treats that have answers that match each pet's number.

㉓ a.

9

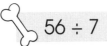 54 ÷ 6

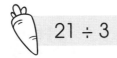 56 ÷ 7

18 ÷ 2

b.

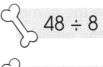 48 ÷ 8

 40 ÷ 5

72 ÷ 9

8

㉔ a.

7

63 ÷ 9

21 ÷ 3

 35 ÷ 7

b.

14 ÷ 2

48 ÷ 8

 24 ÷ 4

6

㉕ a.

5

45 ÷ 9

10 ÷ 2

24 ÷ 6

b.

32 ÷ 8

15 ÷ 3

 20 ÷ 5

4

㉖ a.

3

20 ÷ 5

27 ÷ 9

 24 ÷ 8

b.

18 ÷ 9

18 ÷ 6

 14 ÷ 7

2

7 Division without Remainders

• dividing 2-digit numbers without remainders

**Each part of a division problem has a name.
The three main parts are:**

• **dividend** – the number to be divided
• **divisor** – the number that divides
• **quotient** – the answer

quotient

long division symbol

divisor dividend

Example Name each part of the division problem.

$$28 \div 7 = 4$$

dividend divisor quotient

Try It

$10 \div 5 = 2$

10: _____

5: _____

2: _____

Write the long division for each. Then find the answer.

① $15 \div 3 =$ _____

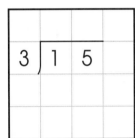

3) 1 5

② $18 \div 6 =$ _____

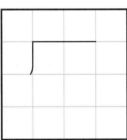

Hints

Long division is one way to do division.

e.g. $12 \div 3 = ?$

divisor (outside the ⌐)

dividend (inside the ⌐)

③ $27 \div 9 =$ _____

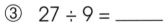

④ $45 \div 5 =$ _____

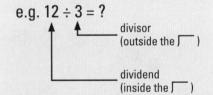

tens	ones
	4 ← quotient
3) 1	2 ← dividend
1	2

divisor →

Think

$3 \times 4 = 12$

the answer

Put 4 in the ones column.

⑤ $56 \div 7 =$ _____

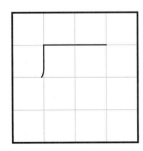

⑥ $16 \div 4 =$ _____

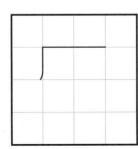

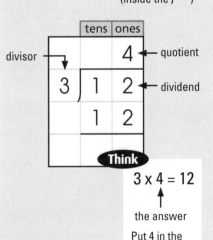
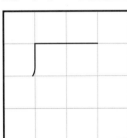

Do the division.

⑦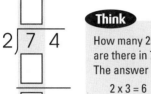

Think
How many 2s are there in 7?
The answer is 3.
2 x 3 = 6
7 − 6 = 1

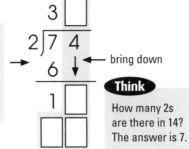 ← bring down

Think
How many 2s are there in 14?
The answer is 7.
2 x 7 = 14

Steps to do long division:

❶ Divide.

❷ Subtract.

❸ Bring it down.

❹ Repeat from ❶ until all the digits are divided.

e.g. 34 ÷ 2 = ?

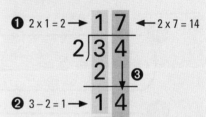

So, 34 ÷ 2 = 17.

⑧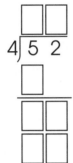
3) 4 5

⑨ 4) 5 2

⑩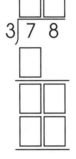
3) 7 8

Find the answers. Show your work.

⑪ 63 ÷ 3 = _____

⑫ 85 ÷ 5 = _____

⑬ 66 ÷ 6 = _____

⑭ 75 ÷ 5 = _____

⑮ 54 ÷ 2 = _____

⑯ 96 ÷ 8 = _____

⑰ 98 ÷ 7 = _____

⑱ 84 ÷ 6 = _____

⑲ 72 ÷ 4 = _____

Do the division.

⑳ $32 \div 2 =$ _____

㉑ $84 \div 7 =$ _____

㉒ $64 \div 4 =$ _____

㉓ $72 \div 6 =$ _____

㉔ $99 \div 9 =$ _____

㉕ $57 \div 3 =$ _____

㉖ $95 \div 5 =$ _____

㉗ $96 \div 6 =$ _____

㉘ $76 \div 4 =$ _____

Do the division. Then put the objects in order from the one with the greatest answer to the one with the smallest. Write the letters.

㉙

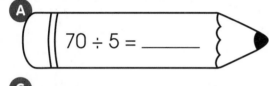
A $70 \div 5 =$ _____

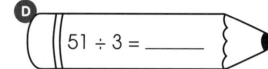
B $56 \div 2 =$ _____

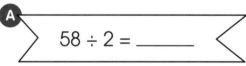
C $66 \div 3 =$ _____

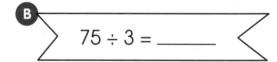
D $51 \div 3 =$ _____

In order: _____

㉚

A $58 \div 2 =$ _____

B $75 \div 3 =$ _____

C $68 \div 4 =$ _____

D $80 \div 5 =$ _____

In order: _____

㉛

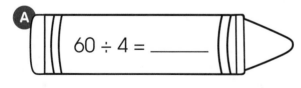
A $60 \div 4 =$ _____

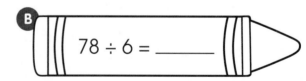
B $78 \div 6 =$ _____

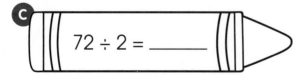
C $72 \div 2 =$ _____

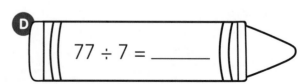
D $77 \div 7 =$ _____

In order: _____

Help the children divide the objects into groups.

③②

I have 48 candies. How many candies will there be in each bag if I divide them equally into...

a. 2 bags?   b. 3 bags?   c. 4 bags?

_____ candies   _____ candies   _____ candies

③③

I have 60 bows. How many bows will each bin have if I divide them equally into...

a. 3 bins?   b. 4 bins?   c. 5 bins?

_____ bows   _____ bows   _____ bows

③④

I have 72 pens. How many pens will each box contain if I divide them equally into...

a. 2 boxes?   b. 4 boxes?   c. 6 boxes?

_____ pens   _____ pens   _____ pens

8 Division with Remainders

- dividing 2-digit numbers with remainders

Read This

A remainder is the quantity left over after a division.

Example Draw circles to do the division.

$14 \div 4 = ?$

3 equal groups   2 left over

$14 \div 4 = 3R2$

quotient   remainder

Try It

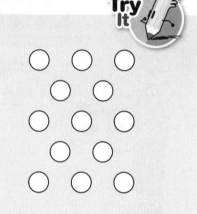

$13 \div 5 = \boxed{} R \boxed{}$

Circle the marbles in each group to do the division.

① $7 \div 2 = \underline{} R \underline{}$

② $8 \div 3 = \underline{}$

③ $14 \div 3 = \underline{}$

④

$16 \div 5 = \underline{}$

⑤

$20 \div 3 = \underline{}$

⑥

$18 \div 4 = \underline{}$

⑦

$17 \div 3 = \underline{}$

Do the division.

⑧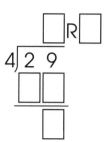

⑨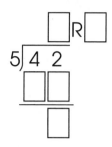

Hints

When doing long division, write the remainder as shown below.

e.g.

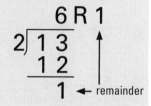

$$13 \div 2 = \underline{6R1}$$

⑩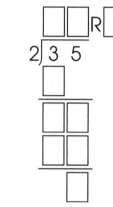

⑪

Find the answers. Show your work.

⑫
$$26 \div 5 = \underline{\quad R \quad}$$

$$5\overline{)2\,6}$$

⑬
$$34 \div 7 = \underline{\qquad}$$

⑭
$$65 \div 8 = \underline{\qquad}$$

⑮
$$43 \div 3 = \underline{\qquad}$$

⑯
$$52 \div 3 = \underline{\qquad}$$

⑰
$$29 \div 2 = \underline{\qquad}$$

Do the division.

⑱ $46 \div 6 =$ _____

⑲ $35 \div 3 =$ _____

⑳ $84 \div 8 =$ _____

㉑ $69 \div 5 =$ _____

㉒ $73 \div 2 =$ _____

㉓ $45 \div 6 =$ _____

㉔ $94 \div 7 =$ _____

㉕ $19 \div 3 =$ _____

㉖ $50 \div 4 =$ _____

㉗ $28 \div 5 =$ _____

The children are dividing objects. Match to show the correct remainder for each problem.

㉘ $19 \div 4$ •

  $16 \div 6$ •

  $23 \div 7$ •

  $22 \div 9$ •

  $18 \div 5$ •

  $42 \div 8$ •

•

•

•

㉙ $87 \div 6$ •

  $74 \div 5$ •

  $81 \div 7$ •

  $50 \div 4$ •

  $38 \div 3$ •

  $68 \div 5$ •

•

•

•

Help Baby Bear find his way to Mother Bear by circling the division problems that have been done correctly.

Multiplication and Division Facts to 81

• relating multiplication and division facts to 81

 Read This Knowing multiplication and division fact families can help you do calculations more efficiently.

Example Cross out the one that is not related to the given fact.

 2 x 3 = 6

○ 3 x 2 = 6   ○ 6 ÷ 2 = 3

○ 6 ÷ 3 = 2   ⊗ 6 – 2 = 4

Try It

4 x 3 = 12

Ⓐ 12 ÷ 4 = 3

Ⓑ 12 ÷ 6 = 2

Ⓒ 3 x 4 = 12

Ⓓ 12 ÷ 3 = 4

Check the related facts.

① 5 x 4 = 20

Ⓐ 20 ÷ 5 = 4

Ⓑ 5 – 4 = 1

② 24 ÷ 6 = 4

Ⓐ 6 x 2 = 12

Ⓑ 6 x 4 = 24

③ 9 x 5 = 45

Ⓐ 9 + 5 = 14

Ⓑ 45 ÷ 9 = 5

④ 21 ÷ 7 = 3

Ⓐ 7 x 4 = 28

Ⓑ 21 ÷ 3 = 7

⑤ 81 ÷ 9 = 9

Ⓐ 9 + 9 = 18

Ⓑ 9 x 9 = 81

⑥ 8 x 2 = 16

Ⓐ 8 – 2 = 6

Ⓑ 2 x 8 = 16

Draw lines to match the related facts.

⑦ 4 x 4 = 16 •

5 x 5 = 25 •

9 x 3 = 27 •

4 x 8 = 32 •

8 x 2 = 16 •

6 x 2 = 12 •

• 25 ÷ 5 = 5

• 8 x 4 = 32

• 16 ÷ 4 = 4

• 27 ÷ 3 = 9

• 12 ÷ 6 = 2

• 16 ÷ 2 = 8

Write the related facts for each given fact.

⑧ 6 x 5 = 30

____ X ____ = ____

____ ÷ ____ = ____

____ ÷ ____ = ____

⑨ 7 x 3 = 21

_____

_____

_____

⑩ 9 x 2 = 18

_____

_____

_____

⑪ 48 ÷ 6 = 8

_____

_____

_____

⑫ 56 ÷ 7 = 8

_____

_____

_____

⑬ 35 ÷ 5 = 7

_____

_____

_____

Write the related facts for each set of numbers.

⑭
4
5
20
_____
_____
_____
_____

⑮
6
3
18
_____
_____
_____
_____

⑯
7
35
5
_____
_____
_____
_____

⑰
8
48
6
_____
_____
_____
_____

⑱
9
7
63
_____
_____
_____
_____

⑲
4
36
9
_____
_____
_____
_____

Find the answers. Then write the related multiplication and division sentences.

⑳ $7 \times 6 = \boxed{}$

_____

_____

_____

㉑ $8 \times 5 = \boxed{}$

_____

_____

_____

㉒ $5 \times 6 = \boxed{}$

_____

_____

_____

㉓ $9 \times 4 = \boxed{}$

_____

_____

_____

㉔ $2 \times 8 = \boxed{}$

_____

_____

_____

㉕ $6 \times 3 = \boxed{}$

_____

_____

_____

Fill in the missing numbers.

㉖ _____ x 5 = 45

$45 \div 5 =$ _____

㉗ 6 x _____ = 24

$24 \div$ _____ = 6

㉘ _____ x 4 = 32

$32 \div$ _____ = 4

㉙ 7 x _____ = 35

$35 \div$ _____ = 7

㉚ _____ x 4 = 36

$36 \div 4 =$ _____

㉛ _____ x 3 = 27

$27 \div 3 =$ _____

㉜ _____ x 9 = 63

$63 \div 9 =$ _____

㉝ 2 x _____ = 14

$14 \div$ _____ = 2

㉞ 6 x _____ = 18

$18 \div$ _____ = 6

㉟ 5 x _____ = 15

$15 \div$ _____ = 5

㊱ _____ x 6 = 42

$42 \div 6 =$ _____

㊲ 7 x _____ = 56

$56 \div$ _____ = 7

To decode Sophia's message, colour the 3 related facts in each set. Then write the letters in order in the blanks.

㊳

START HERE

$9 \times 3 = 27$ **T**	$6 \times 5 = 30$ **O**	$7 + 8 = 15$ **P**
$9 + 3 = 12$ **K**	$6 - 5 = 1$ **J**	$7 \times 8 = 56$ **Y**
$3 \times 9 = 27$ **H**	$30 \div 5 = 6$ **N**	$56 \div 7 = 8$ **W**
$27 \div 3 = 9$ **E**	$5 \times 6 = 30$ **L**	$8 \times 7 = 56$ **A**

$35 \div 5 = 7$ **R**	$6 \times 7 = 42$ **L**	$8 + 5 = 13$ **Q**
$7 \times 5 = 35$ **N**	$6 \times 1 = 6$ **I**	$8 \times 5 = 40$ **Y**
$5 \times 2 = 10$ **S**	$42 \div 6 = 7$ **E**	$40 \div 8 = 5$ **T**
$5 \times 7 = 35$ **M**	$42 \div 7 = 6$ **A**	$40 \div 5 = 8$ **O**

$8 \times 6 = 48$ **A**	$3 \times 7 = 21$ **D**	$9 \times 8 = 72$ **A**
$48 \div 3 = 16$ **T**	$21 \div 7 = 3$ **O**	$8 + 9 = 17$ **X**
$48 \div 8 = 6$ **T**	$7 + 3 = 10$ **V**	$8 \times 9 = 72$ **T**
$6 \times 8 = 48$ **H**	$7 \times 3 = 21$ **M**	$72 \div 8 = 9$ **H**

___ ___ ___   ___ ___ ___ ___   ___ ___ ___

___ ___   ___ ___ ___ ___ ___   ___ ___ ___ ___

IS TO ___ ___   ___ ___ ___ ___!

10 Multiplication and Division (1)

- multiplying and dividing numbers by 10, 100, and 1000

Read This When a number is multiplied or divided by 10, 100, or 1000, add or drop the correct number of zeros to find the answer.

Example Do the multiplication.

3 x 1**0** = 3**0**
⌐———⌐ x 10, so add 1 zero

3 x 1**00** = 3**00**
⌐———⌐ x 100, so add 2 zeros

3 x 1**000** = 3**000**
⌐———⌐ x 1000, so add 3 zeros

Try It

5 x 10 = _____

5 x 100 = _____

5 x 1000 = _____

Do the multiplication.

① **x 10**

1 x 10 = _____

2 x 10 = _____

3 x 10 = _____

4 x 10 = _____

5 x 10 = _____

6 x 10 = _____

7 x 10 = _____

8 x 10 = _____

9 x 10 = _____

10 x 10 = _____

② **x 100**

1 x 100 = _____

2 x 100 = _____

3 x 100 = _____

4 x 100 = _____

5 x 100 = _____

6 x 100 = _____

7 x 100 = _____

8 x 100 = _____

9 x 100 = _____

10 x 100 = _____

③ **x 1000**

1 x 1000 = _____

2 x 1000 = _____

3 x 1000 = _____

4 x 1000 = _____

5 x 1000 = _____

6 x 1000 = _____

7 x 1000 = _____

8 x 1000 = _____

9 x 1000 = _____

10 x 1000 = _____

Find the answers.

④   30 x 10   = _____

⑤   400 x 10   = _____

⑥   70 x 1000 = _____

⑦   10 x 100   = _____

⑧   20 x 10   = _____

⑨   700 x 100 = _____

⑩   8000 x 10 = _____

⑪   9 x 1000   = _____

Fill in the missing numbers.

⑫   90 x _____ = 900

⑬   _____ x 100 = 700

⑭   _____ x 10 = 8000

⑮   50 x _____ = 5000

⑯   2 x _____ = 200

⑰   _____ x 10 = 3000

⑱   4 x _____ = 4000

⑲   700 x _____ = 7000

Do the division.

Tips

When dividing a number by 10, drop 1 zero; when dividing by 100, drop 2 zeros.

e.g.   900 ÷ 10 = 90
        90Ø ⤴

900 ÷ 100 = 9
      9ØØ ⤴

⑳

÷ 10

20 ÷ 10 = _____

400 ÷ 10 = _____

900 ÷ 10 = _____

60 ÷ 10 = _____

800 ÷ 10 = _____

1000 ÷ 10 = _____

7000 ÷ 10 = _____

90 000 ÷ 10 = _____

70 ÷ 10 = _____

㉑

÷ 100

800 ÷ 100 = _____

9000 ÷ 100 = _____

40 000 ÷ 100 = _____

5000 ÷ 100 = _____

600 000 ÷ 100 = _____

Do the multiplication and division.

㉒ 200 x 10 = _____

㉓ 70 x 1000 = _____

㉔ 6000 ÷ 100 = _____

㉕ 900 ÷ 100 = _____

㉖ 700 ÷ 10 = _____

㉗ 40 x 100 = _____

㉘ 8000 ÷ 100 = _____

㉙ 50 x 1000 = _____

㉚ 30 x 10 = _____

㉛ 100 000 ÷ 100 = _____

㉜ 7000 ÷ 10 = _____

㉝ 2000 x 10 = _____

Draw lines to connect the multiplication and division questions that have the same answers.

㉞ 9000 ÷ 10   •   • 1 x 7

700 ÷ 100   •   • 100 x 8

50 000 ÷ 10   •   • 9 x 10

8000 ÷ 10   •   • 1000 x 5

90 ÷ 10   •   • 9 x 1

500 ÷ 100   •   • 7 x 100

7000 ÷ 100   •   • 9 x 100

800 ÷ 100   •   • 5 x 10

5000 ÷ 100   •   • 10 x 7

900 ÷ 10   •   • 1 x 8

7000 ÷ 10   •   • 5 x 1

Fill in the circles with "×" or "÷" to complete the equations.

㉟ 7000 ◯ 100 = 70

㊱ 10 ◯ 1000 = 10 000

㊲ 50 ◯ 10 = 500

㊳ 400 ◯ 100 = 4

㊴ 600 ◯ 100 = 6

㊵ 800 ◯ 10 = 8000

㊶ 20 ◯ 1000 = 20 000

㊷ 9000 ◯ 100 = 90

㊸ 30 000 ◯ 10 = 3000

㊹ 7000 ◯ 10 = 70 000

Colour the boxes that have correct answers to guide the boy through the maze.

㊺

8000 ÷ 8 = 100	100 ÷ 10 = 1	3 x 10 = 300
600 x 10 = 6000	2 x 1000 = 2000	4000 ÷ 100 = 40
70 ÷ 10 = 7	9 x 100 = 9000	500 ÷ 100 = 5
4 x 100 = 400		8000 ÷ 10 = 800
		90 x 10 = 900
9000 ÷ 100 = 90	60 000 ÷ 10 = 6000	100 x 100 = 10 000
20 x 10 = 200		7000 ÷ 10 = 1000
7000 ÷ 100 = 70		600 ÷ 100 = 60
500 x 10 = 5000	10 000 ÷ 10 = 100	200 x 10 = 200
80 x 100 = 8000		
100 000 ÷ 100 = 1000	200 x 100 = 20 000	
2000 ÷ 10 = 20	40 x 100 = 1000	

11 Multiplication and Division (2)

• multiplying and dividing 2-digit numbers

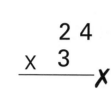 **This**

When you multiply or divide, remember to align the numbers to the right.

Example 24 x 3 = ?

$$
\begin{array}{r}
2\ 4 \\
\times\ \ \ 3 \\
\hline
\end{array}
$$

$$
\begin{array}{r}
2\ 4 \\
\times\ \ \ 3 \\
\hline
7\ 2
\end{array} \quad \checkmark
$$

align

3 x 2 + 1 = 7 ⟶   ⟵ 3 x 4 = 12; 2 in
the ones place
and 1 carried over

24 x 3 = [72]

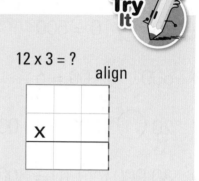

Try It

12 x 3 = ?

align

$$
\begin{array}{r}
 \\
\times
\end{array}
$$

12 x 3 = [   ]

Do the multiplication. Show your work.

①
$$
\begin{array}{r}
2\ 1 \\
\times\ \ \ 4 \\
\hline
\ \ \ \ \ \
\end{array}
$$

21 x 4 = _____

② 32 x 3 = _____

③ 16 x 6 = _____

④ 19 x 5 = _____

⑤ 35 x 4 = _____

⑥ 43 x 4 = _____

⑦ 26 x 9 = _____

⑧ 18 x 3 = _____

⑨ 32 x 9 = _____

Do the division. Show your work.

⑩ $72 \div 8 =$ _____

⑪ $45 \div 3 =$ _____

⑫ $52 \div 4 =$ _____

⑬ $99 \div 9 =$ _____

⑭ $60 \div 4 =$ _____

⑮ $91 \div 7 =$ _____

⑯ $70 \div 5 =$ _____

⑰ $81 \div 3 =$ _____

⑱ $26 \div 2 =$ _____

Do the multiplication and division. Find and colour the answers on the court to help Michelle get her basketball.

⑲ a. $15 \times 2 =$ _____

b. $36 \div 3 =$ _____

c. $46 \div 2 =$ _____

d. $25 \times 5 =$ _____

e. $87 \div 3 =$ _____

f. $91 \div 7 =$ _____

g. $13 \times 8 =$ _____

h. $34 \times 4 =$ _____

i. $76 \div 4 =$ _____

j. $28 \times 5 =$ _____

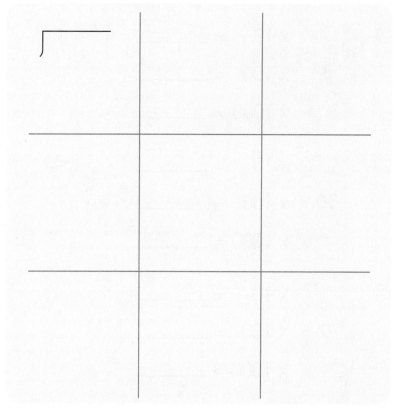

33	17	49	50	23
83	92	53	88	125
12	140	30	19	29
104	5	28	100	25
13	91	81	20	111
136	27	35	16	46

Do the multiplication.

㉑
8	x 10 =	_____
	x 100 =	_____
	x 1000 =	_____

㉑
29	x 10 =	_____
	x 100 =	_____
	x 1000 =	_____

㉒
30	x 10 =	_____
	x 100 =	_____
	x 1000 =	_____

㉓
15	x 10 =	_____
	x 100 =	_____
	x 1000 =	_____

㉔
0	x 10 =	_____
	x 100 =	_____
	x 1000 =	_____

㉕
1	x 10 =	_____
	x 100 =	_____
	x 1000 =	_____

Do the division to complete the tables.

㉖

	÷ 10	÷ 100
200		
3000		
900		
60 000		
500		
7000		
100 000		
2000		
800		

㉗

	÷ 10	÷ 100
1300		
42 000		
5100		
991 000		
3700		
98 000		
25 100		
469 800		
101 100		

Write the correct letters in the blank puzzle pieces to complete the number sentences.

㉘

300 ⌇ ⌇ = 3000

300 ⌇ ⌇ = 30 000

3000 ⌇ ⌇ = 30

300 ⌇ ⌇ = 30

Please help me put these puzzle pieces in the correct places.

A ⌇ x 10 ⌇

B ⌇ x 100 ⌇

C ⌇ x 1000 ⌇

D ⌇ ÷ 10 ⌇

E ⌇ ÷ 100 ⌇

㉙

11 ⌇ ⌇ = 110

11 000 ⌇ ⌇ = 1100

1100 ⌇ ⌇ = 1100

1100 ⌇ ⌇ = 110 000

1100 ⌇ ⌇ = 11

A ⌇ x 10 ⌇

B ⌇ x 100 ⌇

C ⌇ x 1000 ⌇

D ⌇ ÷ 10 ⌇

E ⌇ ÷ 100 ⌇

F ⌇ x 1 ⌇

12 Fractions

• representing and comparing parts of a whole with fractions

Read This

Fractions are used to describe the equal parts of a whole.

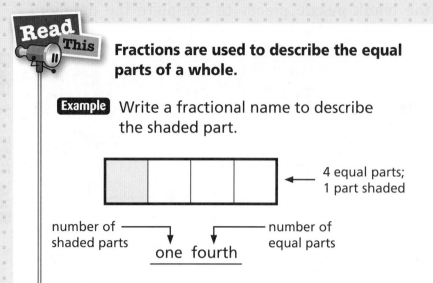

Example Write a fractional name to describe the shaded part.

4 equal parts; 1 part shaded

number of shaded parts ——→ one fourth ←—— number of equal parts

Try It

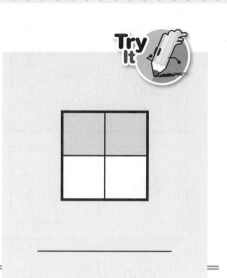

_____

Write a fractional name to describe the shaded part of each diagram.

①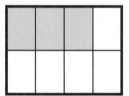

_____

②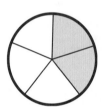

_____

③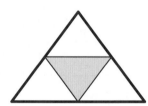

_____

④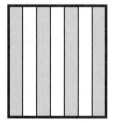

_____

⑤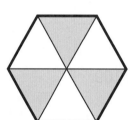

_____

⑥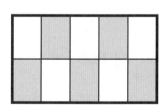

_____

Colour the correct number of parts to show each fraction.

⑦ one half

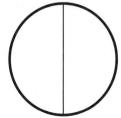

⑧ three fifths

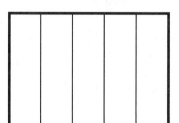

⑨ five eighths

Circle the fraction that describes the shaded part of each diagram.

⑩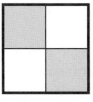

$\frac{2}{4}$ $\frac{4}{2}$

⑪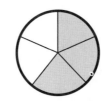

$\frac{3}{5}$ $\frac{2}{5}$

 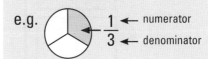
⑫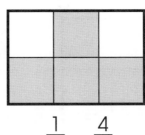

$\frac{2}{3}$ $\frac{3}{3}$

⑬

$\frac{1}{6}$ $\frac{4}{6}$

Write a fraction to describe the shaded part of each diagram.

⑭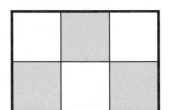

_____

⑮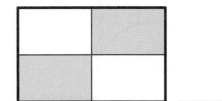

_____

⑯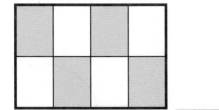

_____

⑰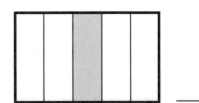

_____

⑱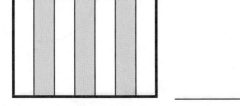

_____

⑲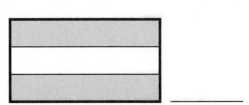

_____

⑳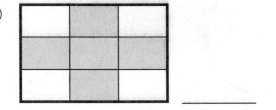

_____

㉑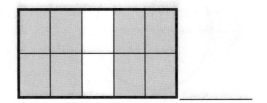

_____

Write fractions to describe the shaded parts in the picture.

㉒

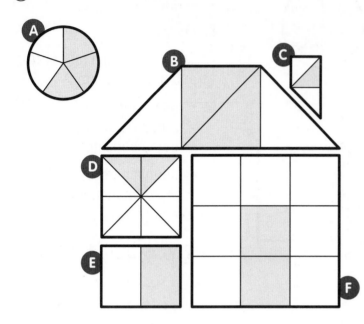

A _____   B _____

C _____   D _____

E _____   F _____

Colour the correct number of parts to show each fraction.

㉓ $\frac{1}{2}$

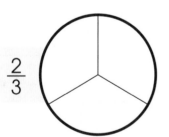

㉔ $\frac{3}{4}$

㉕ $\frac{2}{7}$

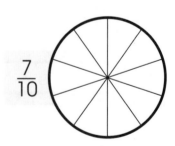

㉖ $\frac{2}{3}$

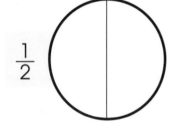

㉗ $\frac{3}{5}$

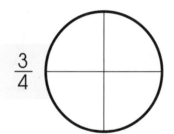

㉘ $\frac{7}{10}$

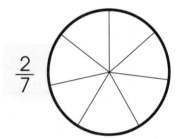

㉙ $\frac{6}{8}$

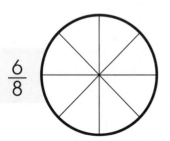

㉚ $\frac{5}{6}$

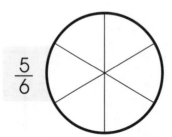

㉛ $\frac{4}{9}$

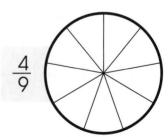

Colour to show each pair of fractions. If the fractions are equivalent, put a check mark; if not, put a cross.

 $\dfrac{3}{4}$ $\dfrac{6}{8}$ $\dfrac{1}{3}$ $\dfrac{2}{6}$

$\dfrac{3}{4} = \dfrac{6}{8}$ ◯ $\dfrac{1}{3} = \dfrac{2}{6}$ ◯

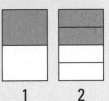

Hints

Equivalent fractions are fractions that represent the same value.

e.g.

$\dfrac{1}{2} = \dfrac{2}{4}$

So, $\dfrac{1}{2}$ and $\dfrac{2}{4}$ are equivalent fractions.

Colour to show each pair of fractions. Then compare them and put ">" or "<" in the circle.

㉞ 
$\dfrac{3}{5}$
$\dfrac{4}{5}$

$\dfrac{3}{5}$ ◯ $\dfrac{4}{5}$

Tips

> greater than

< less than

e.g. 10 > 1
    1 < 10

㉟ $\dfrac{6}{10}$
$\dfrac{4}{5}$
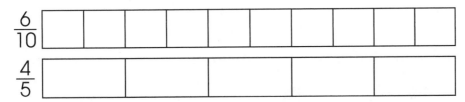

$\dfrac{6}{10}$ ◯ $\dfrac{4}{5}$

㊱ $\dfrac{4}{9}$
$\dfrac{2}{3}$
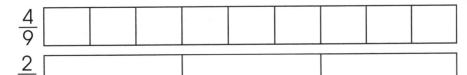

$\dfrac{4}{9}$ ◯ $\dfrac{2}{3}$

㊲ $\dfrac{5}{8}$
$\dfrac{2}{4}$
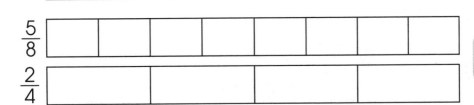

$\dfrac{5}{8}$ ◯ $\dfrac{2}{4}$

13 Decimals

- representing and comparing parts of a whole with decimals

Read This

A decimal number has two parts – a whole number part and a decimal part. These two parts are separated by a dot (.) called the decimal point.

e.g.

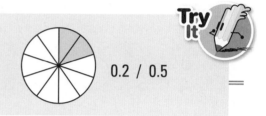

Example Circle the decimal that describes the shaded part of the diagram.

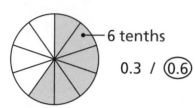

6 tenths

0.3 / (0.6)

Try It

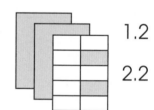

0.2 / 0.5

Circle the decimal that describes the shaded part of each diagram.

① 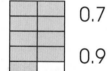 0.7 0.9

② 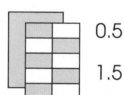 0.5 1.5

③ 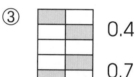 0.4 0.7

④ 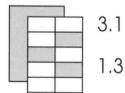 3.1 1.3

⑤ 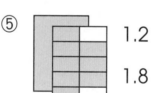 1.2 1.8

⑥ 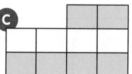 1.2 2.2

Write a decimal for the shaded part of each diagram.

⑦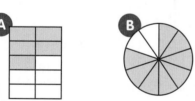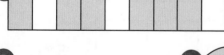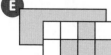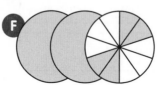

Decimals

Ⓐ _____

Ⓑ _____

Ⓒ _____

Ⓓ _____

Ⓔ _____

Ⓕ _____

Colour to show each decimal.

⑧ **1.8**
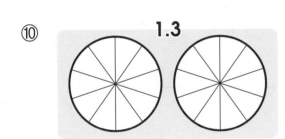

⑪ **2.3**
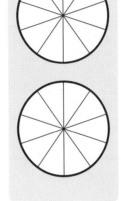

⑫ **1.9**
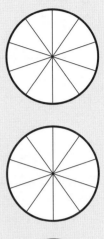

⑨ **0.7**

⑩ **1.3**

Complete each number line by counting forward by 0.1's. Then locate each decimal.

⑬ **1.5**
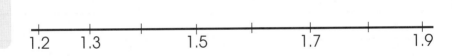
1.2   1.3   1.5   1.7   1.9

⑭ **2.2**
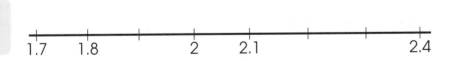
1.7   1.8   2   2.1   2.4

⑮ **3.1**
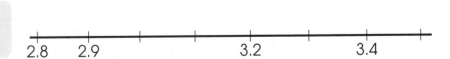
2.8   2.9   3.2   3.4

⑯ **4.5**

3.9   4.1   4.4

⑰ **5.7**

5.4   5.5   6

Locate the decimals on each number line. Then put ">" or "<" in the circle.

⑱

0.8 ◯ 1.2

Tips The decimal that is farther to the left is smaller; the one that is farther to the right is greater.

⑲

1.7 ◯ 2.9

⑳

1.8 ◯ 2.1   3.2 ◯ 2.9

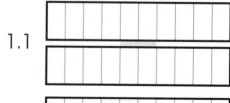

Colour the diagrams to represent each pair of decimals. Then compare the decimals and circle the greater one.

㉑
0.5

0.7

㉒
0.8

0.2

㉓
1.4

1.8

㉔
1.1

0.9

Compare each pair of decimals. Circle the correct decimal.

㉕ **the greater decimal**

a. 0.2   0.7   b. 1.5   0.9

c. 3.4   4.3   d. 1.8   2

e. 0.5   1.3   f. 2.4   2.7

㉖ **the smaller decimal**

a. 0.4   0.3   b. 1.2   0.5

c. 2.3   2.5   d. 1.3   3.1

e. 2.2   3.3   f. 3.5   4.5

Hints

To compare decimals, compare the digits in the same place value from left to right.

e.g.

ones	tenths
1	4
2	1

2 > 1

So, 2.1 is greater.

ones	tenths
1	4
1	6

the same   6 > 4

So, 1.6 is greater.

Compare each pair of decimals. Put ">" or "<" in the circle.

㉗ 2.6 ◯ 2.7   ㉘ 1.4 ◯ 2.3   ㉙ 0.5 ◯ 0.1

㉚ 3.1 ◯ 1.9   ㉛ 2.5 ◯ 2.2   ㉜ 3.6 ◯ 3

㉝ 1.3 ◯ 1.8   ㉞ 0.4 ◯ 0.3   ㉟ 1.2 ◯ 2.1

Put the decimals in the correct order.

㊱ **smallest to greatest**

a. 0.3   1.1   0.2   1.3

_____

b. 3.2   2.4   4.3   2.3

_____

㊲ **greatest to smallest**

a. 0.8   1.3   1   2.5

_____

b. 1.5   3.1   3.5   1.3

_____

14 Fractions and Decimals

- understanding how fractions and decimals are related

 This

Both fractions and decimals describe parts of a whole. They are closely related to each other.

Example Write a fraction and a decimal to describe the shaded part.

fraction: $\frac{7}{10}$

decimal: 0.7

10 parts in all; 7 parts shaded

Try It

_____ _____
fraction   decimal

Write a fraction and a decimal for the shaded part of each diagram.

①

_____ _____
fraction   decimal

②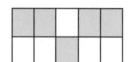

_____ _____

③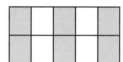

_____ _____

④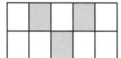

_____ _____

⑤

_____ _____

⑥

_____ _____

⑦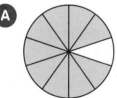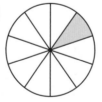

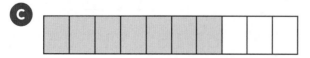

	Fraction	Decimal
A	_____	_____
B	_____	_____
C	_____	_____

Colour to show each decimal. Then write each decimal in words and as a fraction.

⑧

| 0.6 | | fraction: |

In words:

⑨

| 0.5 | | fraction: |

In words:

⑩

| 0.9 | | fraction: |

In words:

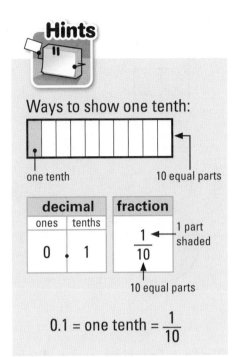

Hints

Ways to show one tenth:

one tenth   10 equal parts

decimal		fraction
ones	tenths	$\frac{1}{10}$ ← 1 part shaded
0	1	

10 equal parts

$0.1 = $ one tenth $= \frac{1}{10}$

Colour to show each fraction. Draw lines so that each diagram has 10 equal parts. Then write an equivalent fraction and decimal for each coloured diagram.

⑪ $\frac{1}{5}$

equivalent fraction ____   decimal ____

⑫ $\frac{4}{5}$

____   ____

⑬ $\frac{2}{5}$

____   ____

⑭ $\frac{1}{2}$

____   ____

Can you see that one fifth is the same as two tenths?

$\frac{1}{5}$

$\frac{2}{10}$

Write a fraction and a decimal for the shaded part of each diagram.

⑮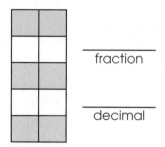

fraction

_____

decimal

⑯ 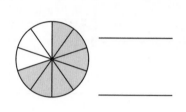 _____

_____

⑰ 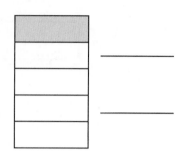 _____

_____

⑱ 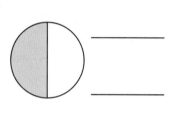 _____

_____

⑲ 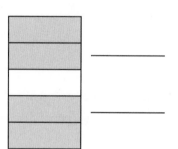 _____

_____

⑳ 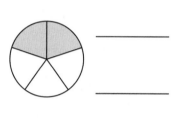 _____

_____

Write a fraction and a decimal for the shaded part of each set of diagrams.

㉑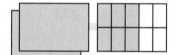

fraction   decimal

㉒

_____ _____

㉓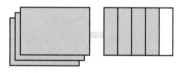

_____ _____

㉔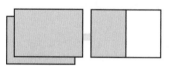

_____ _____

Hints

ones	tenths
1	2

In words:
one and two tenths

$1\frac{2}{10}$ 1.2

fraction   decimal

㉕

_____ _____

㉖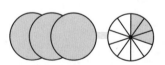

_____ _____

㉗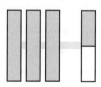

_____ _____

Convert each fraction into a decimal and vice versa. Draw a diagram to support each answer.

㉘ Fraction ➝ Decimal

a.
$$\frac{1}{10} = \underline{\hspace{1cm}}$$

b.
$$\frac{2}{5} = \underline{\hspace{1cm}}$$

c.
$$\frac{1}{2} = \underline{\hspace{1cm}}$$

d.
$$1\frac{3}{10} = \underline{\hspace{1cm}}$$

e.
$$2\frac{4}{5} = \underline{\hspace{1cm}}$$

㉙ Decimal ➝ Fraction

a.
$$0.6 = \underline{\hspace{1cm}}$$

b.
$$0.8 = \underline{\hspace{1cm}}$$

c.
$$0.9 = \underline{\hspace{1cm}}$$

d.
$$1.5 = \underline{\hspace{1cm}}$$

e.
$$1.4 = \underline{\hspace{1cm}}$$

15 Length

• understanding units of length and unit conversions

Choosing an appropriate unit to do measurement is important.

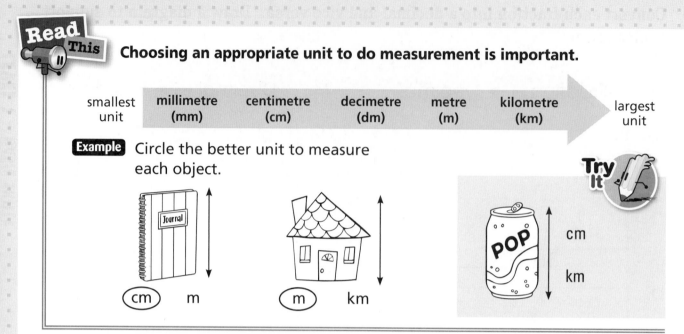

smallest unit → millimetre (mm) | centimetre (cm) | decimetre (dm) | metre (m) | kilometre (km) → largest unit

Example Circle the better unit to measure each object.

Journal — (cm) m

house — (m) km

Try It

POP — cm / km

Write the most appropriate unit of measure for each object.

①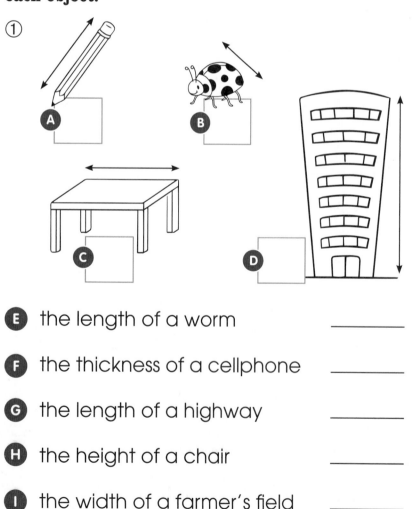

A

B

C

D

E the length of a worm _____

F the thickness of a cellphone _____

G the length of a highway _____

H the height of a chair _____

I the width of a farmer's field _____

Hints

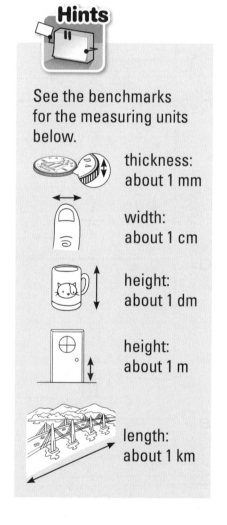

See the benchmarks for the measuring units below.

thickness: about 1 mm

width: about 1 cm

height: about 1 dm

height: about 1 m

length: about 1 km

Measure the crayons with a ruler to find their lengths. Then colour them the specified colours according to their lengths.

②

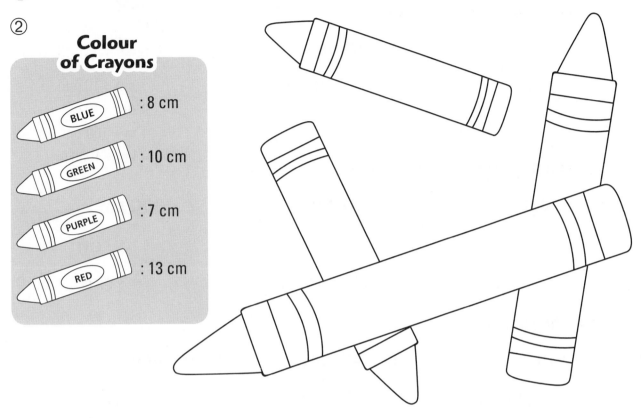

Colour of Crayons

BLUE : 8 cm

GREEN : 10 cm

PURPLE : 7 cm

RED : 13 cm

Measure the lines with a ruler. Record their lengths in "cm" and "mm".

Length

centimetres   millimetres

③

A _____ _____ _____

B _____ _____ _____

C _____ _____ _____

D _____ _____ _____

E _____ _____ _____

F _____ _____ _____

Check the correct conversions of the given measurements.

④ **millimetre and centimetre**

a. **3 cm**
- (A) 30 mm
- (B) 300 mm

b. **70 mm**
- (A) 700 cm
- (B) 7 cm

Hints

1 cm = 10 mm
1 dm = 10 cm
1 m = 100 cm
1 km = 1000 m

⑤ **centimetre and decimetre**

a. **8 dm**
- (A) 800 cm
- (B) 80 cm

b. **40 cm**
- (A) 4 dm
- (B) 400 dm

c. **300 cm**
- (A) 30 dm
- (B) 3 dm

⑥ **centimetre and metre**

a. **5 m**
- (A) 500 cm
- (B) 50 m

b. **200 cm**
- (A) 20 m
- (B) 2 m

c. **10 m**
- (A) 100 cm
- (B) 1000 cm

⑦ **metre and kilometre**

a. **4 km**
- (A) 400 m
- (B) 4000 m

b. **6000 m**
- (A) 6 km
- (B) 60 km

c. **13 km**
- (A) 13 000 m
- (B) 1300 m

Do the conversions.

⑧ 6 dm = _____ cm

⑨ 3 cm = _____ mm

⑩ 3 m = _____ cm

⑪ 9 km = _____ m

⑫ 700 mm = _____ cm

⑬ 2 dm = _____ cm

⑭ 40 cm = _____ dm

⑮ 8 km = _____ m

⑯ 5000 m = _____ km

⑰ 900 mm = _____ cm

Circle the more reasonable measurement for each diagram. Then convert it into the given unit.

⑱

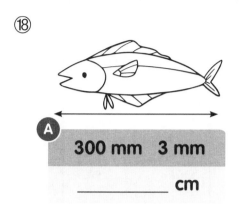

A
300 mm   3 mm

_____ cm

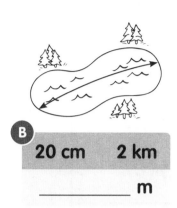

B
20 cm   2 km

_____ m

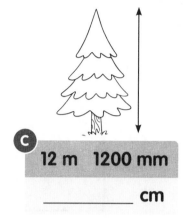

C
12 m   1200 mm

_____ cm

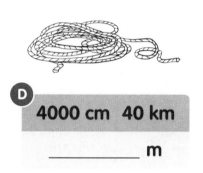

D
4000 cm   40 km

_____ m

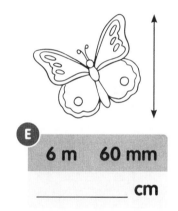

E
6 m   60 mm

_____ cm

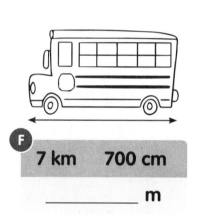

F
7 km   700 cm

_____ m

I'm hiking along this trail to the pond.

G height of the boy
13 m   1300 mm

_____ cm

H length of the trail
2000 m   200 m

_____ km

I perimeter of the map
2 m   20 m

_____ cm

16 Perimeter

• finding the perimeters of polygons in centimetres

Perimeter is the total distance around a shape. It is measured in units of length, such as the centimetre.

Example Find the perimeter.

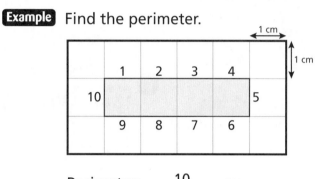

Perimeter: ___10___ cm

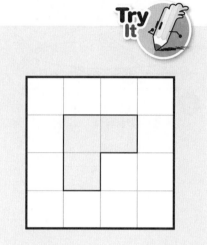

Perimeter: _____ cm

Find the perimeter of the shape on each centimetre grid.

①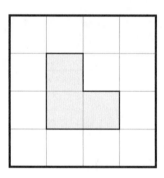

_____ cm

②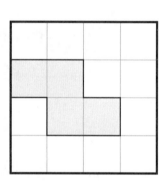

_____

Tips Each square on a centimetre grid measures 1 cm by 1 cm.

③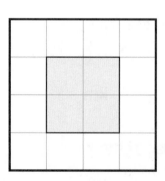

_____

④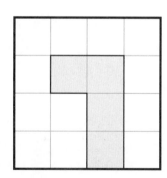

_____

⑤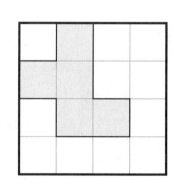

_____

Find the perimeters of the stickers on the centimetre grid. Then draw the shape and answer the questions.

Perimeter

⑥ a. Draw a square sticker that has a perimeter of 16 cm. Add a to the sticker.

Tips

All 4 sides of a square are equal in length.

b. Which stickers have the same perimeter? Circle them.

c. Which sticker has the greatest perimeter? Circle it.

 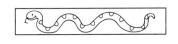

Find the perimeter of each shape. Show your work.

Hints

Add up the lengths of all sides to find the perimeter of a shape.

e.g.

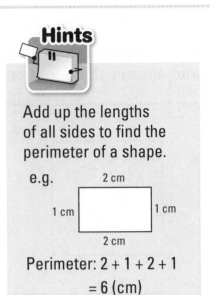

Perimeter: 2 + 1 + 2 + 1
= 6 (cm)

⑦

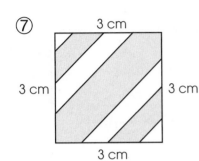

3 cm
3 cm   3 cm
3 cm

Perimeter:

_____ + _____ + _____ + _____

= _____ (cm)

⑧

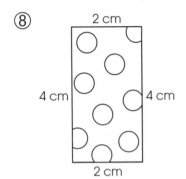

2 cm
4 cm   4 cm
2 cm

Perimeter:

_____

= _____ (cm)

⑨

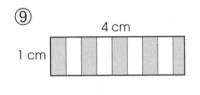

4 cm
1 cm

Perimeter:

_____

= _____ (cm)

⑩

Perimeter

_____

Ⓐ   _____ + _____ + _____ = _____ (cm)

_____

Ⓑ

_____

Ⓒ

_____

Ⓓ

_____

Ⓔ

_____

Ⓕ

_____

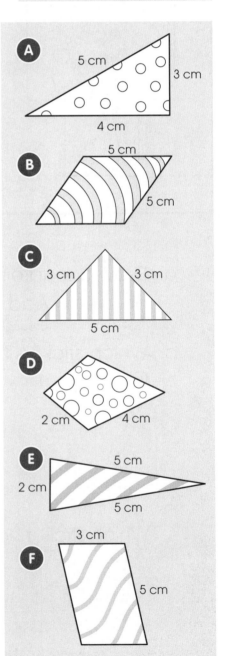

Ⓐ
5 cm   3 cm
4 cm

Ⓑ
5 cm
5 cm

Ⓒ
3 cm   3 cm
5 cm

Ⓓ
2 cm   4 cm

Ⓔ
5 cm
2 cm
5 cm

Ⓕ
3 cm
5 cm

Measure and record the lengths of each shape. Then find the perimeter.

⑪

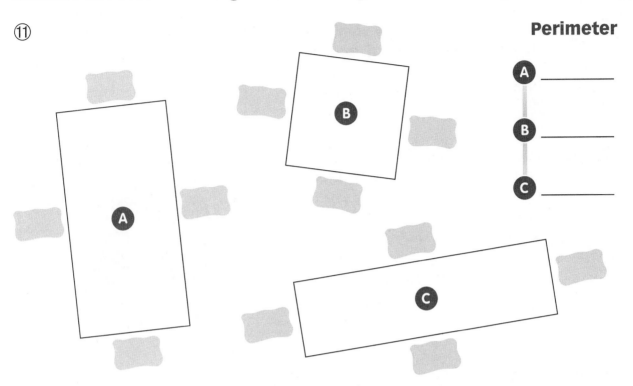

Perimeter

A _____

B _____

C _____

Look at the shapes in the picture. Measure to find the side lengths of each shape. Then find the perimeter.

⑫

Hi!

Perimeter

_____   _____   _____   _____

17 Mass

• understanding the measuring units of mass

Mass tells you how heavy something is. It is commonly measured in milligrams (mg), grams (g), and kilograms (kg).

smallest unit → milligram (mg)　　gram (g)　　kilogram (kg) → largest unit

Example Circle the most appropriate unit for measuring the mass of each object.

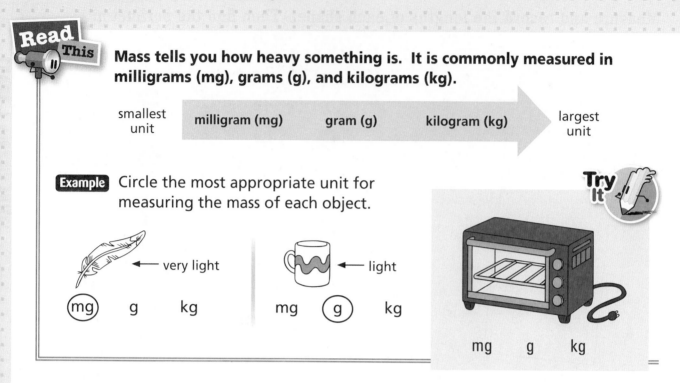

← very light

(mg)　g　kg

← light

mg　(g)　kg

Try It

mg　g　kg

Determine whether the mass of each is best measured in mg, g, or kg.

①

Say cheese!

_____

_____

_____

_____

_____

_____

Circle the better estimate of mass for each object.

②

7 g
1 kg

30 g
50 mg

300 mg
100 g

Tips

 30 mg

 150 g

 1 kg

2 kg
500 mg

20 g
10 kg

200 mg
80 g

300 g
5 kg

5 g
200 g

70 g
800 kg

Do the conversions.

③ **mg ⟷ g**

3 g = _____ mg

2 g = _____ mg

10 g = _____ mg

5000 mg = _____ g

8000 mg = _____ g

4000 mg = _____ g

④ **kg ⟷ g**

6 kg = _____ g

4 kg = _____ g

3 kg = _____ g

7000 g = _____ kg

9000 g = _____ kg

4000 g = _____ kg

Hints

1 g = 1000 mg

1 kg = 1000 g

Do the conversions.

⑤ 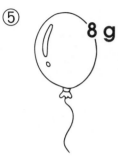 8 g

_____ mg

⑥ 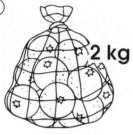 2 kg

_____ g

⑦ 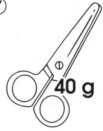 40 g

_____ mg

⑧  Flour 3000 g

_____ kg

⑨  40 000 mg

_____ g

⑩  300 g

_____ mg

⑪  2000 g

_____ kg

⑫  15 g

_____ mg

Circle the correct weight in each pair. Then put the weights in order.

⑬

| heavier | a. 400 g / 2 kg |
| | b. 5000 mg / 3 g |

| lighter | a. 6000 g / 4 kg |
| | b. 7 g / 10 000 mg |

 **Tips** Always compare measurements in the same unit. Do conversions if needed.

⑮ 3 g   300 mg   30 mg

_____ < _____ < _____

⑯ 4000 mg   40 g   4 kg

_____ < _____ < _____

⑰ 800 g   8000 mg   80 kg

_____ > _____ > _____

⑱ 20 000 g   2 kg   200 mg

_____ > _____ > _____

Draw weights to balance each toy. Then answer the questions.

⑲

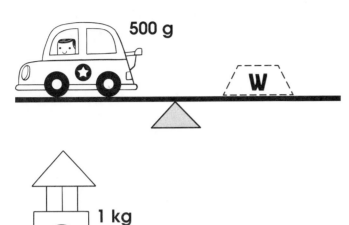

500 g

W

1 kg

Each weight is 250 g.

⑳ How many weights are needed to balance

   a. 2 toy cars? _____

   b. 3 toy towers? _____

㉑ How many toy cars are needed to balance a toy tower? _____

㉒ Look at how many weights are needed to balance each toy below. Find the mass of each toy.

Tips Pay attention to the unit of measurement.

A 2 W

_____ g

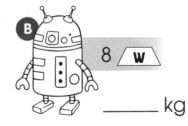

B 8 W

_____ kg

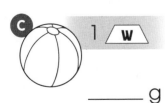

C 1 W

_____ g

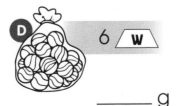

D 6 W

_____ g

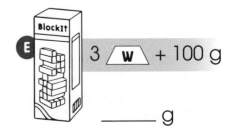

E 3 W + 100 g

_____ g

18 Time

• converting units of time and reading time

Read This

Time can be measured in many units, including minutes, hours, days, and weeks.

Example Circle the units of time.

(minute)   centimetre   (century)

kilogram   (hour)   litre

(second)   °C   gram

Try It

day   milligram

week   metre

millilitre   year

Check the correct answers.

① **2 hours**
- Ⓐ 120 minutes
- Ⓑ 120 seconds

② **4 minutes**
- Ⓐ 40 seconds
- Ⓑ 240 seconds

③ **2 days**
- Ⓐ 14 hours
- Ⓑ 48 hours

④ **4 weeks**
- Ⓐ 28 days
- Ⓑ 240 days

⑤ **3 years**
- Ⓐ 30 months
- Ⓑ 36 months

⑥ **2 years**
- Ⓐ 104 weeks
- Ⓑ 14 weeks

⑦ **4 hours**
- Ⓐ 240 minutes
- Ⓑ 28 minutes

⑧ **3 decades**
- Ⓐ 300 years
- Ⓑ 30 years

⑨ **4 centuries**
- Ⓐ 40 years
- Ⓑ 400 years

⑩ **2 centuries**
- Ⓐ 20 decades
- Ⓑ 200 decades

⑪ **6 hours**
- Ⓐ 360 minutes
- Ⓑ 42 minutes

Hints

Relationships between different units of time:

1 minute = 60 seconds

1 hour = 60 minutes

1 day = 24 hours

1 week = 7 days

1 year = 365/366 days
  = 52 weeks
  = 12 months

1 decade = 10 years

1 century = 100 years
  = 10 decades

Do the conversions and fill in the blanks.

⑫ 2 minutes = _____ seconds   ⑬ 3 hours = _____ minutes

⑭ 6 days = _____ hours   ⑮ 72 hours = _____ days

⑯ 10 minutes = _____ seconds   ⑰ 8 hours = _____ minutes

⑱ 120 seconds = _____ minutes   ⑲ 240 minutes = _____ hours

⑳  It took _____ hours (120 minutes) for the water to freeze in the freezer.

㉑ 3 weeks = _____ days   ㉒ 28 days = _____ weeks

㉓ 2 years = _____ months   ㉔ 4 years = _____ weeks

㉕ 7 weeks = _____ days   ㉖ 104 weeks = _____ years

㉗ 36 months = _____ years   ㉘ 5 weeks = _____ days

㉙  It took Grandma _____ weeks (14 days) to knit this scarf for me.

㉚ 4 decades = _____ years   ㉛ 3 centuries = _____ years

㉜ 5 decades = _____ years   ㉝ 6 centuries = _____ decades

㉞ 10 decades = _____ years   ㉟ 7 centuries = _____ decades

㊱  The castle I visited in England was built more than _____ years (5 centuries) ago.

Read and record the times.

A _____ : _____

B _____

C _____

D _____

E _____

F _____

G _____

H _____

Read about Nolan's schedule. Draw clock hands to show the times.

This is my schedule for today.

Nolan

8:05
breakfast

3:15
hockey

9:40
bedtime

Complete the calendars and find the answers.

 39

FEBRUARY 2020

SUN	MON	TUE	WED	THU	FRI	SAT
						1
2	3		5			8
	10	11	12		14	
		18		20		22
	24		26			29

MARCH 2020

SUN	MON	TUE	WED	THU	FRI	SAT
1	2		4	5		
	9	10			13	14
	16				20	
		24	25	26		
29						

APRIL 2020

SUN	MON	TUE	WED	THU	FRI	SAT
			1	2		
	6	7		9	10	
12		14	15			18
19	20	21			24	
			29	30		

a. Circle the dates.

- February 3, 2020
- February 15, 2020
- the last day in February
- March 7, 2020
- March 25, 2020
- the third Sunday in March
- April 5, 2020
- April 23, 2020
- the last Sunday in April

b. Write the dates.

- the first day in April

_____

- the second Friday in February

_____

- the fourth Tuesday in March

_____

c. Write the days of the week.

- February 18, 2020

_____

- March 12, 2020

_____

- April 11, 2020

_____

19 Shapes

- identifying quadrilaterals and their properties

Shapes that are made of 4 straight sides are called quadrilaterals.

Example Check the quadrilateral.

Try It

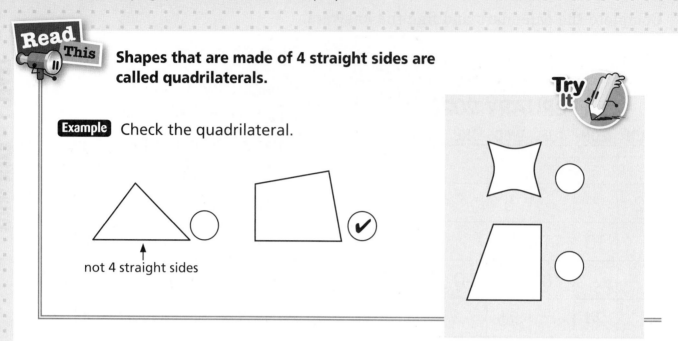

not 4 straight sides

Colour the quadrilaterals and name them.

①

Quadrilaterals

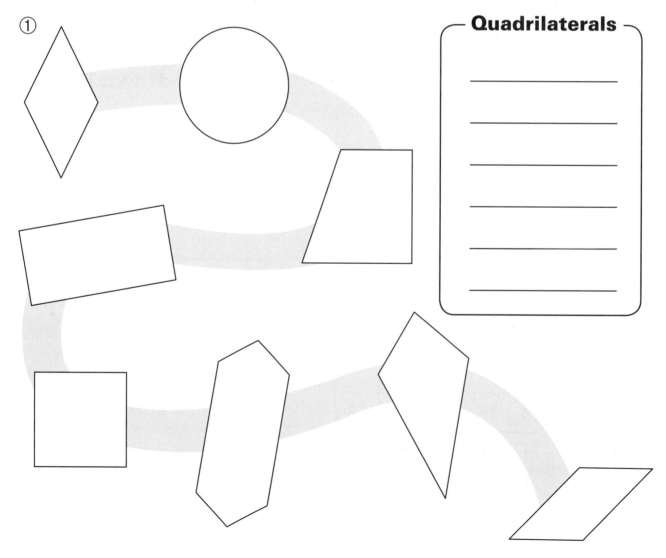

_____

_____

_____

_____

_____

Trace the lines of the quadrilaterals as specified.

② Trace the pairs of parallel sides using a different colour for each pair.

Tips Parallel sides are sides of a shape that will never intersect even when extended.

e.g.

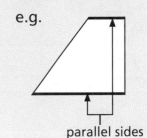

parallel sides

③ Trace the equal sides using a different colour for each set.

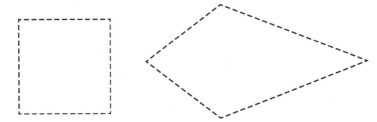

For each quadrilateral, draw all lines of symmetry. Then circle the quadrilaterals that have right angles.

④

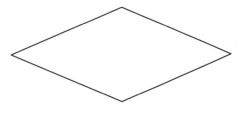

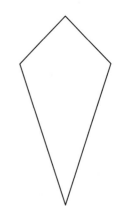

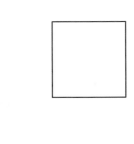

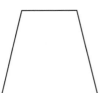

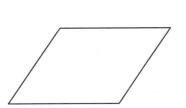

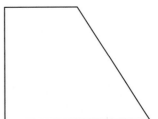

Check the properties each quadrilateral has in the table.

⑤

	equal sides	parallel sides	right angle	line of symmetry
☐				
▭				
▱				
⬠				
◇				
◇				

Tips Below are the properties of some common quadrilaterals.

equal sides: sides that have the same length

parallel sides: sides that are parallel

right angle: a 90° angle

line of symmetry: a line that divides a shape into 2 halves

Sketch each shape in the box. Then write the numbers to show its properties.

⑥ **square**

- _____ equal sides
- _____ pair(s) of parallel sides
- _____ right angle(s)
- _____ line(s) of symmetry

⑧ **rhombus**

- _____ equal sides
- _____ pair(s) of parallel sides
- _____ right angle(s)
- _____ line(s) of symmetry

⑦ **kite**

- _____ pair(s) of equal sides
- _____ pair(s) of parallel sides
- _____ right angle(s)
- _____ line(s) of symmetry

Circle "T" for the true statements and "F" for the false ones.

⑨ Quadrilaterals can have 4 or more sides as long as they are all straight sides. **T / F**

⑩ All trapezoids have one pair of parallel sides. **T / F**

⑪ All trapezoids have right angles. **T / F**

⑫ All kites have a line of symmetry. **T / F**

⑬ All squares have 4 equal sides. **T / F**

⑭ A trapezoid that has 1 line of symmetry does not have right angles. **T / F**

Name and sketch a quadrilateral with each given set of properties.

⑮
- all sides equal
- 4 lines of symmetry

⑯
- 1 line of symmetry
- no parallel sides

⑰
This one has 2 answers. Show both. 
- 2 lines of symmetry
- 2 pairs of parallel sides

20 Solids

- naming solids and identifying their properties

To determine whether a solid is a prism or a pyramid, check the number of bases that it has.

Example Colour the base(s) of the solids.

 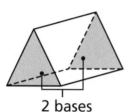

1 base   2 bases

Try It

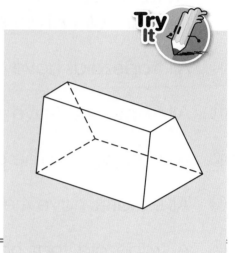

Colour the base(s) of each solid. Then name the solid.

①  _____

② 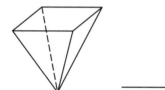 _____

Hints

A prism has two bases of the same shape.

e.g.  prism

A pyramid has one base.

e.g. 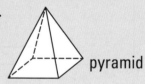 pyramid

③ Ⓐ 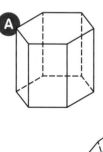   Ⓑ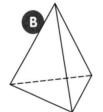

Ⓒ    Ⓓ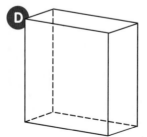

Ⓐ _____

Ⓑ _____

Ⓒ _____

Ⓓ _____

Write the letters to match the solids with their names. Then count and write the number of faces, vertices, and edges each one has.

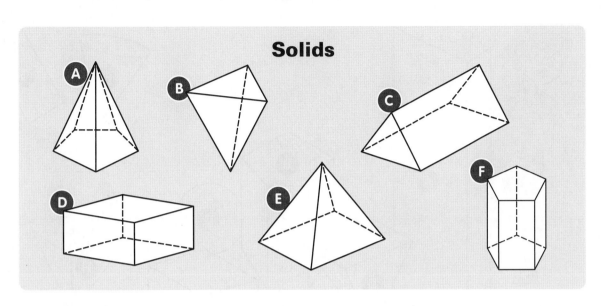

Solids

④ Solid ☐ rectangular pyramid

 • _____ faces

 • _____ vertices

 • _____ edges

⑤ Solid ☐ triangular prism

 • _____ faces

 • _____ vertices

 • _____ edges

⑥ Solid ☐ pentagonal pyramid

 • _____ faces

 • _____ vertices

 • _____ edges

⑦ Solid ☐ rectangular prism

 • _____ faces

 • _____ vertices

 • _____ edges

⑧ Solid ☐ triangular pyramid

 • _____ faces

 • _____ vertices

 • _____ edges

⑨ Solid ☐ pentagonal prism

 • _____ faces

 • _____ vertices

 • _____ edges

List the solids with the given properties to complete the table. Then answer the questions.

⑩

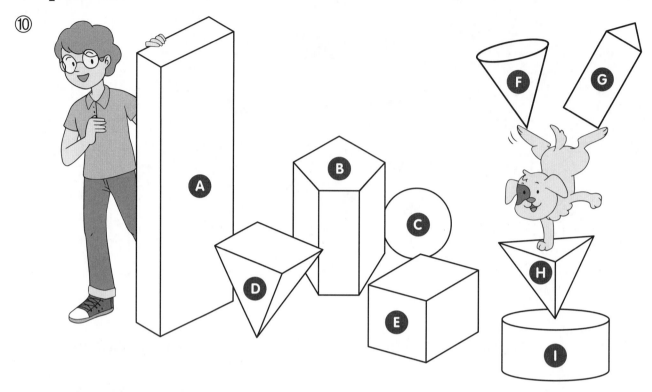

Property	Solid
has exactly 6 vertices	
has exactly 10 vertices	
has 8 or more edges	
has rectangular faces	
has triangular faces	
has rectangular and triangular faces	

a. Which solids can be stacked?

_____

b. Which solids can slide and roll?

_____

c. Which solid has a rectangular face but cannot be stacked?

_____

d. Which solid cannot be stacked but can roll?

_____

Read the descriptions of each solid. Sketch the solid being described and name it. Then answer the questions.

⑪
- has 8 vertices
- has no triangular faces

_____

⑫
- has 6 vertices
- has 5 triangular faces

_____

⑬
- has 6 edges
- has only triangular faces

_____

⑭
- has 8 vertices
- has only square faces

_____

⑮

I want to make one of the solids mentioned above. If I use 6 balls of modelling clay for the vertices and 10 sticks for the edges, which solid can I make?

_____

⑯ Which two solids have the same number of vertices, edges, and faces?

_____

21 Grid Maps

• locating objects and describing movements on grid maps

 **Read This**

A grid map is divided by lines into rows and columns. The columns are labelled with letters and the rows are labelled with numbers.

Example Which object is located at A2?

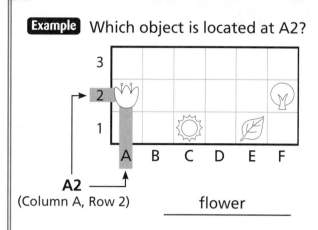

A2 ——→
(Column A, Row 2)

flower _____

Try It

Which object is located at E1?

_____

Look at the map. Then locate the objects.

①

a. Name the objects with the given coordinates.

   • A3: _____

   • B5: _____

   • C2: _____

   • D1: _____

b. Write the coordinates of the objects.

   • grapes: _____

   • watermelon: _____

   • strawberry: _____

   • mango: _____

Use the grid map to answer the questions.

②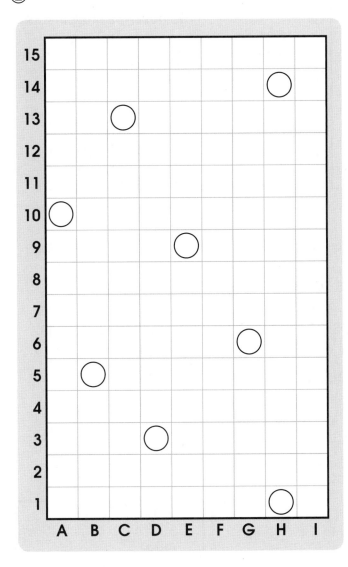

a. Write the coordinates of the circles.

_____

_____

_____

b. Draw a △ at these coordinates:

F4	D8	A14	H7
B9	C1	E9	I12

c. At which coordinates do two shapes overlap?

_____

d. What are the coordinates of the two circles that are 13 squares apart vertically?

_____

③ Draw a rectangle at G14.

a. What shape is the closest to it? _____

b. What are the coordinates of that shape? _____

④ Draw a square at A5.

a. What shape is the closest to it? _____

b. What are the coordinates of that shape? _____

Draw the shapes and find the answers.

Hints

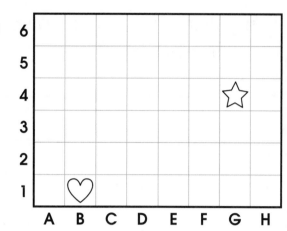

To describe movements on grid maps, use the words "up", "down", "left", and "right".

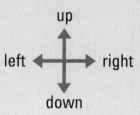

a. Draw the shapes.

- Move the ♡ 3 squares to the right and 2 squares up.

- Move the ☆ 4 squares to the left and 3 squares down.

b. What are the new coordinates of the shapes?

- ♡: _____

- ☆: _____

Describe the movements.

⑥ a.  to 📏 :

He goes _____

_____ .

b. 😊 to ✂ :

_____

_____

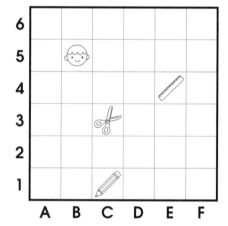

c. 😊 to ✏ : _____

d. If 😊 wants to be at F6, how should he go?

_____

Draw the missing objects on the grid. Then describe the movements.

⑦

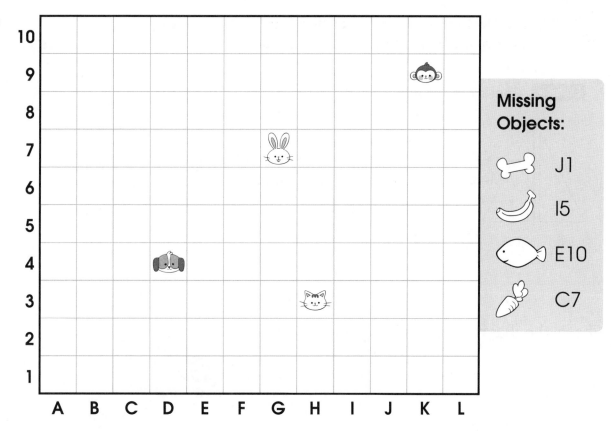

Missing Objects:

J1

I5

E10

C7

Describe the movement of each animal to its favourite food.

a. to : The rabbit goes _____

_____ to reach the carrot.

b. to : _____

_____

c. to : _____

_____

d. to : _____

_____

22 Reflections

- identifying and completing reflections

Read This

A reflection is a transformation that flips a shape over a line, creating a mirrored image.

Example Check the reflection.

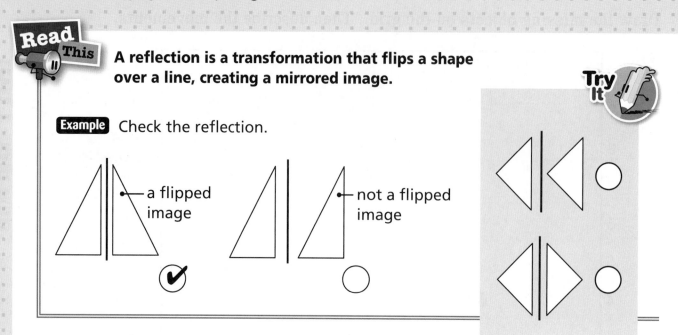

a flipped image ✔

not a flipped image ○

Try It

Check the diagrams that show reflections.

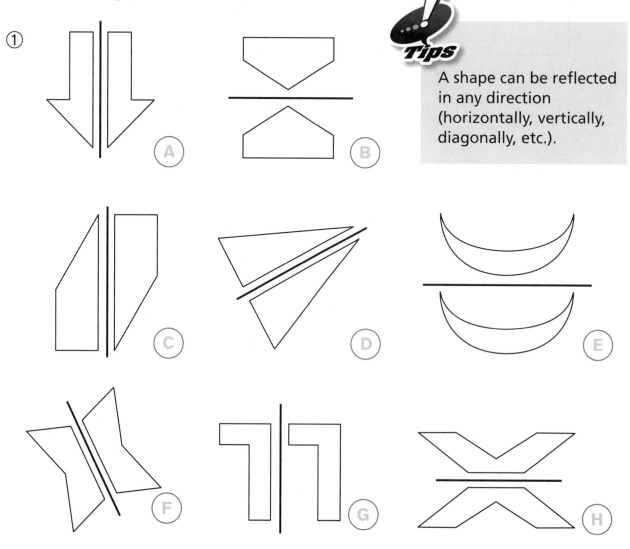

Tips

A shape can be reflected in any direction (horizontally, vertically, diagonally, etc.).

Draw the reflected image of each shape.

②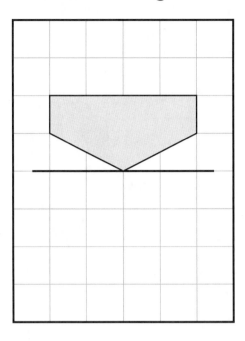

Tips The vertices of a shape and the corresponding vertices of its image are always the same distances from the line of reflection.

e.g.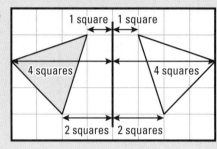

③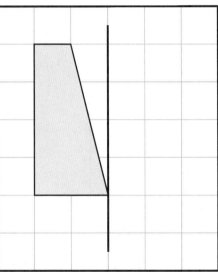

④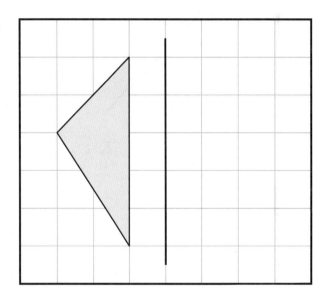

⑤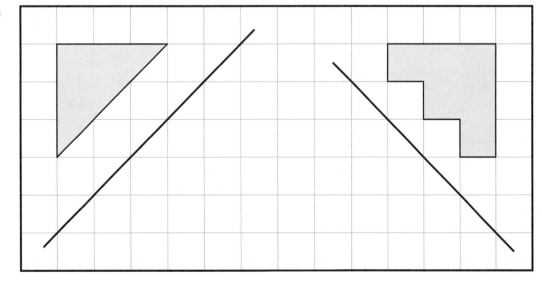

Reflect each shape and draw its image.

⑥

Count the number of dots a shape is from the line of reflection to help locate its reflection.

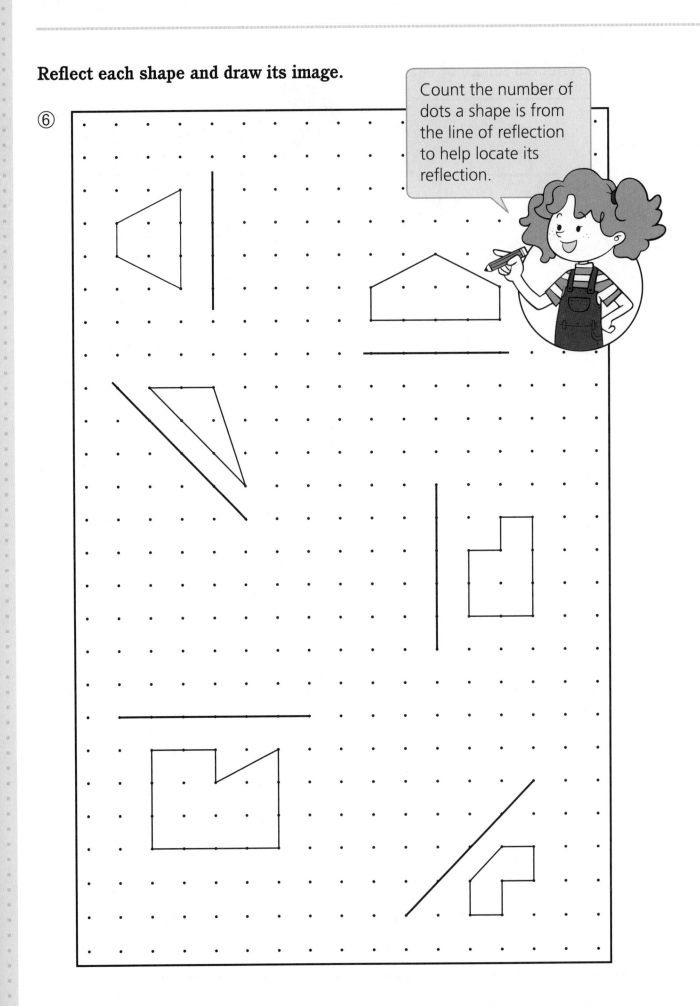

Fill in the blanks to describe the reflections. Then do the reflection.

⑦ a. From ⌊ to ⌋ :

Reflect ⌊ in Line _____ .

b. From ⌊ to ⌈ :

Reflect ⌊ _____ .

c. Reflect ⌈ in Line C.

Do the reflections as described. Then answer the question.

⑧

Reflect ◿ in Line X. Label the image **A** . ➡ Reflect **A** in Line Y. Label the image **B** . ➡ Reflect **B** in Line Z. Label the image **C** .

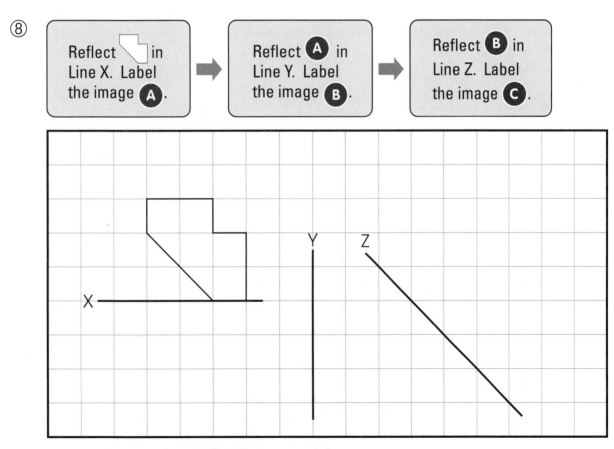

Are the images **A** , **B** , and **C** congruent? _____

23 Data Management

• understanding the median and the mode

Read This

The median is the middle value of a set of data that is in order; the mode is the value that appears most often.

Example Find the median and the mode of each set of data.

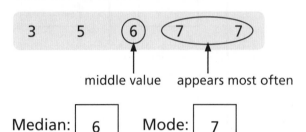

middle value   appears most often

Median: 6   Mode: 7

Try It

2   4   4   4   5

Median: ☐   Mode: ☐

Find the median and the mode of each set of data.

① 2   5   5   5   7

_____ _____
median   mode

② 2   2   2   5   5   6   6

_____ _____
median   mode

③ 3   3   3   4   4

_____ _____
median   mode

④ 10   10   11   12   13

_____ _____
median   mode

⑤ 4   5   5   7   7

_____ _____
median   mode

⑥ 8   9   9   11   11   12

_____ _____
median   mode

⑦ 1   1   3   3   5   5   5   7

_____ _____
median   mode

Hints

⑧ 2   2   2   3   3   4   4   4

_____ _____
median   mode

When there are two middle values, add them and divide the sum by 2 to find the median.

e.g. 3 4 ⑤ ⑦ 7 9

$(5 + 7) \div 2 = 6$

So, the median is 6.

Put each set of data in order from smallest to greatest. Then find the median and the mode.

⑨
4   3   5   6   4   3   4

In order

Median: _____

Mode: _____

⑩
6   8   1   3   1   4   8   1   9

In order

Median: _____

Mode: _____

⑪
7   10   6   5   6   6   10

In order

Median: _____

Mode: _____

⑫
9   12   4   12   9   9   4

In order

Median: _____

Mode: _____

Read what the children say. Match them with the correct sets of data.

⑬

Ⓐ 10   9   12   7   12 | Ⓑ 12   10   13   12   10

Ⓒ 11   13   11   12   11 | Ⓓ 6   8   10   6   10   10

  10 is the only mode in this set of data.   _____

  12 is the median in this set of data.   _____

  The median is 10.   _____

  The median is the same as the mode.   _____

Read each problem. Find the median and the mode.

⑭ Elsa surveyed 5 families on the number of children each family has.

Number of Children in Each Family

| 2 | 4 | 3 | 1 | 2 |

Median: _____ children

Mode: _____ children

⑮ Jason recorded the number of trees in 6 parks.

Number of Trees in Each Park

| 20 | 15 | 19 | 13 | 15 | 14 |

Median: _____

Mode: _____

⑯ Lory recorded the number of apples in baskets at the apple orchard.

Number of Apples in Each Basket

| 12 | 14 | 15 | 14 | 12 |
| 12 | 12 | 12 | 14 | 15 |

Median: _____

Mode: _____

⑰ Marilyn recorded the weights of 12 dogs in kilograms.

Weight of Each Dog (kg)

| 12 | 24 | 15 | 16 | 13 | 15 |
| 15 | 12 | 13 | 14 | 15 | 25 |

Median: _____

Mode: _____

⑱ Ms. Linda recorded the number of points her students got in a Math contest.

Number of Points Each Student Got

86	86	90	93	72	76
90	74	94	92	74	71
76	96	79	74	86	82

Median: _____

Mode: _____

The fish are lined up according to their weights. Read what they say to find the missing weights.

⑲
The median of our weights is 2 kg and the modes are 1 kg and 3 kg.

1 kg   _____   _____   3 kg   _____

⑳
Both the median and mode of our weights are 2 kg.

1 kg   _____   _____   2 kg   3 kg

Find each missing piece of data using the given information.

㉑ The median is 4 and the mode is 5.

5	3	6
2	4	3
5	☐	5

㉒ The median is 13 and the mode is 12.

18	12	☐
8	5	14
16	21	13

㉓ The median is 16 and the mode is 15.

14	16	20	14
20	15	15	21
☐	21	19	15

㉔ The median is 10 and the mode is 11.

12	11	12	6
4	5	6	11
11	8	11	☐

LEVEL 2
FURTHER YOUR UNDERSTANDING

1 Addition and Subtraction

• adding and subtracting 4-digit numbers

When adding or subtracting whole numbers, remember to write the numbers so that each place value lines up vertically. Work from the right to the left, starting with the ones place.

e.g.

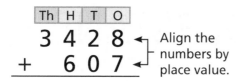

Align the numbers by place value.

Example 3428 + 607 = ?

Start with the ones place.

$$
\begin{array}{r}
① \quad ① \\
3\ 4\ 2\ 8 \\
+\ \ \ 6\ 0\ 7 \\
\hline
4\ 0\ 3\ 5
\end{array}
$$

3428 + 607 = 4035

Try It

2817 – 352 = ?

Find the answers. Show your work.

① a. 6548 + 525 = _____

   b. 1160 + 419 = _____

   c. 4182 + 537 = _____

   d. 5755 + 308 = _____

② a. 6721 – 563 = _____

   b. 8464 – 285 = _____

   c. 7641 – 852 = _____

   d. 2586 – 497 = _____

+ _____

− _____

Find the answers. Show your work. Then decode to see what John says.

③ 4800 − 1200 = _____ h

5360 − 1250 = _____ n

2317 + 2503 = _____ f

2425 + 1293 = _____ u

5000 − 1200 = _____ i

2600 − 1580 = _____ h

2367 + 1425 = _____ a

5123 − 1354 = _____ u

4444 − 1666 = _____ c

2008 + 1994 = _____ s

2463 + 558 = _____ t

889 + 225 = _____ s

John

M‾‾‾‾‾ ‾‾‾‾‾ ‾‾‾‾‾ ‾‾‾‾‾ ‾‾‾‾‾
 3792   3021   1020   3800   4002

‾‾‾‾‾ ‾‾‾‾‾ ‾‾‾‾‾ ‾‾‾‾‾   ‾‾‾‾‾ ‾‾‾‾‾ ‾‾‾‾‾!
1114 3718 2778 3600   4820 3769 4110

Find the answers. Then use addition or subtraction to check each answer.

Hints

④
```
  3 2 1 7
+ 1 3 8 0
```

Check
```
[        ]

- 1 3 8 0

[        ]
```
Use subtraction to check addition.

You may use addition to check the answer to a subtraction question and vice versa.

e.g.
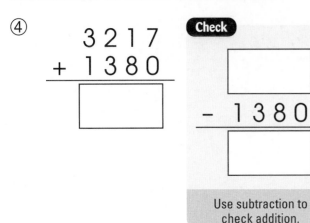
```
   2 4 6 2        Check    2 7 8 3
 +   3 2 1               -   3 2 1
   2 7 8 3                 2 4 6 2  ← the same ✔
```

So, the answer 2783 is correct.

⑤
```
  5 7 8 0
- 4 1 9 2
```
Check

```
[        ]
```

⑥
```
  3 6 0 9
+ 2 7 9 4
```
Check

```
[        ]
```

⑦
```
  1 8 2 7
+ 3 4 9 3
```
Check

```
[        ]
```

⑧
```
  7 0 2 1
- 1 4 3 6
```
Check

```
[        ]
```

Look at Andy's work. Check the questions with correct answers. Cross out the ones that are wrong and write the correct answers above the incorrect ones.

⑨

Ⓐ 1078 – 780 = _298_

Ⓑ 3089 + 128 = _3317_

Ⓒ 9985 – 813 = _9272_

Ⓓ 6106 + 914 = _7020_

Ⓔ 5549 + 472 = _6022_

Ⓕ 5319 – 1482 = _3837_

Ⓖ 4193 + 927 = _5110_

Ⓗ 3279 – 368 = _2811_

Ⓘ 1160 + 466 = _1626_

Ⓙ 8461 – 7587 = _874_

Find the answer. Then use estimation to figure out if your answer is reasonable.

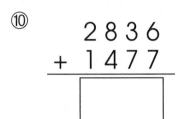

⑩
```
  2 8 3 6
+ 1 4 7 7
```
Estimate

Tips To estimate, round each number to the nearest hundred. Then add or subtract.

⑪
```
  3 0 2 4
-   9 1 6
```
Estimate

⑫
```
  8 1 1 7
- 3 2 9 3
```
Estimate

⑬
```
  2 3 6 7
+ 3 3 4 9
```
Estimate

⑭
```
  4 6 2 3
+ 1 6 5 7
```
Estimate

Round each number to the nearest hundred. Estimate each answer and then find the actual answer.

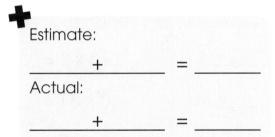

⑮   3217 ➔ _____

1948 ➔ _____

Estimate:

_____ + _____ = _____

Actual:

_____ + _____ = _____

Estimate:

_____ - _____ = _____

Actual:

_____ - _____ = _____

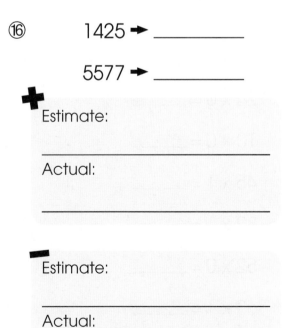

⑯   1425 ➔ _____

5577 ➔ _____

Estimate:

_____

Actual:

_____

Estimate:

_____

Actual:

_____

2 Multiplication

• multiplying numbers, including 0 and 1

The product of any number and 0 is always 0. The product of any number and 1 is always the number itself.

Example Do the multiplication.

8 x 0 = [0]   12 x 0 = [0]

8 x 1 = [8]   12 x 1 = [12]

 Try It

7 x 0 = [ ]   21 x 1 = [ ]

19 x 1 = [ ]   1 x 36 = [ ]

Read what the girl says and find the answers.

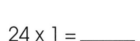 Try to complete this activity in 1 minute. Ready, set, go!

① 9 x 0 = _____

42 x 1 = _____

20 x 1 = _____

33 x 0 = _____	24 x 1 = _____	0 x 34 = _____
24 x 0 = _____	12 x 0 = _____	18 x 1 = _____
10 x 0 = _____	1 x 34 = _____	13 x 1 = _____
45 x 1 = _____	1 x 40 = _____	0 x 31 = _____
32 x 1 = _____	19 x 0 = _____	0 x 37 = _____
52 x 0 = _____	27 x 0 = _____	16 x 1 = _____
63 x 1 = _____	1 x 82 = _____	0 x 57 = _____
78 x 0 = _____	29 x 0 = _____	69 x 1 = _____

Do the multiplication.

②

Multiplication Table

	1	2	3	4	5	6	7	8	9
1	1	2	3	4	5	6	7	8	9
2	2	4	6	8	10	12	14	16	18
3	3	6	9	12	15	18	21	24	27
4	4	8	12	16	20	24	28	32	36
5	5	10	15	20	25	30	35	40	45
6	6	12	18	24	30	36	42	48	54
7	7	14	21	28	35	42	49	56	63
8	8	16	24	32	40	48	56	64	72
9	9	18	27	36	45	54	63	72	81

Use the multiplication table to help you complete Levels 1, 2, and 3! Better yet, memorize the table. It will make multiplying easier in the future!

Level 1

2 x 1 = _____

4 x 3 = _____

7 x 0 = _____

1 x 5 = _____

6 x 2 = _____

4 x 1 = _____

0 x 7 = _____

1 x 3 = _____

5 x 4 = _____

7 x 2 = _____

Level 2

8 x 3 = _____

7 x 5 = _____

6 x 9 = _____

9 x 1 = _____

4 x 8 = _____

0 x 7 = _____

9 x 3 = _____

4 x 6 = _____

5 x 8 = _____

7 x 3 = _____

Level 3

9 x 7 = _____

8 x 8 = _____

9 x 9 = _____

6 x 8 = _____

8 x 7 = _____

4 x 9 = _____

7 x 7 = _____

5 x 9 = _____

7 x 5 = _____

8 x 5 = _____

Do the multiplication.

③
```
    3 4
x     4
```

④
```
    2 3
x     3
```

Tips Remember to regroup when needed.

⑤
```
    3 2
x     9
```

⑥
```
    2 8
x     2
```

⑦
```
    5 7
x     7
```

⑧
```
    4 8
x     9
```

⑨
```
    6 0
x     6
```

⑩
```
    3 9
x     5
```

⑪ 67 x 3 = _____

⑫ 46 x 8 = _____

⑬ 27 x 4 = _____

⑭ 77 x 5 = _____

⑮ 39 x 7 = _____

⑯ 20 x 9 = _____

⑰ 22 x 6 = _____

⑱ 81 x 9 = _____

⑲ 52 x 4 = _____

⑳ 35 x 6 = _____

㉑ 42 x 8 = _____

㉒ 63 x 9 = _____

㉓ 95 x 4 = _____

Do your work here.

Find the product of each pair of numbers. Then colour the
answers in the maze below to see where the boy is going.

㉔

26 7
_____
product

14 8
_____

6 33
_____

5 19
_____

4 36
_____

42 8
_____

18 9
_____

55 2
_____

93 7
_____

237	98	333	450	198
519	702	681	382	112
451	486	95	144	110
64	509	182	514	641
913	972	162	633	87
167	286	651	706	381
99	201	336	600	101

LEVEL 2 – FURTHER YOUR UNDERSTANDING

Solve the problems. Show your work.

㉕

There are 9 apples in each basket. How many apples
are there in

a. 1 basket?   b. 6 baskets?   c. 12 baskets?

_____ apples   _____ apples   _____ apples

㉖

There are 24 stickers on each sheet. How many stickers
are there on

a. 0 sheets?   b. 4 sheets?   c. 9 sheets?

_____ stickers   _____ stickers   _____ stickers

㉗

There are 8 pens in each box. How many pens are
there in

a. 2 boxes?   b. 5 boxes?   c. a dozen boxes?

_____ pens   _____ pens   _____ pens

3 Division

• dividing numbers, including 0 and 1

A number divided by 1 is the number itself.

e.g. $2 \div 1 = 2$

0 divided by a number is always 0.

e.g. $0 \div 5 = 0$

Example Do the division.

$3 \div 1 =$ | 3 |

$82 \div 1 =$ | 82 |

$0 \div 6 =$ | 0 |

$0 \div 18 =$ | 0 |

Try It

$17 \div 1 =$ ☐

$23 \div 1 =$ ☐

$0 \div 5 =$ ☐

$0 \div 9 =$ ☐

Do the division.

① $0 \div 13 =$ _____

② $23 \div 1 =$ _____

③ $0 \div 25 =$ _____

④ $40 \div 1 =$ _____

⑤ $0 \div 1 =$ _____

⑥ $13 \div 1 =$ _____

⑦ $0 \div 2 =$ _____

⑧ $19 \div 1 =$ _____

⑨ $0 \div 30 =$ _____

⑩ $52 \div 1 =$ _____

⑪ $0 \div 91 =$ _____

⑫ $11 \div 1 =$ _____

Fill in the blank to make each division sentence correct.

Hints

0 divided by any number is 0.

e.g. Divide an empty jug of juice into 2 cups.

⑬ $36 \div$ _____ $= 36$

⑭ _____ $\div 5 = 0$

⑮ _____ $\div 1 = 8$

⑯ $10 \div$ _____ $= 10$

⑰ $0 \div 9 =$ _____

⑱ $12 \div$ _____ $= 12$

⑲ _____ $\div 1 = 4$

⑳ _____ $\div 1 = 1$

㉑ $0 \div 5 =$ _____

㉒ $21 \div 1 =$ _____

㉓ _____ $\div 77 = 0$

㉔ $49 \div$ _____ $= 49$

$0 \div 2 = 0$

no juice   2 cups   no juice in each cup

Do the division.

㉕ $3\overline{)63}$ ㉖ $4\overline{)79}$ ㉗ $3\overline{)58}$ ㉘ $2\overline{)43}$

㉙ $7\overline{)84}$ ㉚ $3\overline{)40}$ ㉛ $6\overline{)84}$ ㉜ $5\overline{)97}$

㉝ $36 \div 3 = \underline{\hphantom{xxxx}}$

㉞ $48 \div 5 = \underline{\hphantom{xxxx}}$

㉟ $78 \div 6 = \underline{\hphantom{xxxx}}$

㊱ $29 \div 2 = \underline{\hphantom{xxxx}}$

㊲ $34 \div 3 = \underline{\hphantom{xxxx}}$

㊳ $57 \div 4 = \underline{\hphantom{xxxx}}$

㊴ $76 \div 5 = \underline{\hphantom{xxxx}}$

㊵ $91 \div 3 = \underline{\hphantom{xxxx}}$

㊶ $34 \div 4 = \underline{\hphantom{xxxx}}$

㊷ $69 \div 5 = \underline{\hphantom{xxxx}}$

㊸ $81 \div 7 = \underline{\hphantom{xxxx}}$

Do your work here.

Do the division. Find the letters whose answers have a remainder of 1. Then unscramble them to discover where the key is hidden.

④

7)22	8)99	9)55	5)88
D	A	S	S
3)85	5)71	6)77	4)57
E	R	D	R
8)65	3)35	2)47	7)56
S	O	E	P

The key is hidden in my

☐☐☐☐☐☐☐ .

Adrian completed the quiz below. For each answer, put a check mark if it is correct; otherwise, cross it out and write the correct answer beside it. Then fill in the blank.

④⑤

Math Quiz

Name: _Adrian_

Do the division.

1. $57 \div 3$ = _19_

2. $50 \div 3$ = _16_

3. $96 \div 8$ = _12_

4. $99 \div 8$ = _12R3_

5. $60 \div 7$ = _8R1_

6. $78 \div 5$ = _15R3_

7. $75 \div 4$ = _18R3_

8. $94 \div 3$ = _31R1_

9. $84 \div 5$ = _16R4_

10. $79 \div 5$ = _16R1_

11. $95 \div 6$ = _15R5_

12. $91 \div 6$ = _15R1_

13. $78 \div 3$ = _26_

14. $37 \div 2$ = _18R1_

15. $92 \div 2$ = _46_

16. $69 \div 9$ = _7R6_

17. $85 \div 5$ = _18_

18. $93 \div 6$ = _15R3_

19. $84 \div 3$ = _28_

20. $71 \div 4$ = _17R3_

I got _____ questions right.

4 Multiplication and Division

• multiplying and dividing 2-digit numbers

Multiplication and division are closely related. Use division to check answers to multiplication questions and vice versa.

e.g.
● ● ● ● ●
● ● ● ● ●
● ● ● ● ●
● ● ● ● ●

$$4 \times 5 = 20$$
$$20 \div 4 = 5$$

Try It

Do the math to check each answer. If it is correct, put a check mark; otherwise, put a cross.

Example Use division to check if the multiplication is correct.

$$19 \times 3 = \underline{57}$$

Check $57 \div 3$

$$\begin{array}{r} 19 \\ 3\overline{)57} \\ \underline{3} \\ 27 \\ \underline{27} \end{array}$$ ← same as in the multiplication

The multiplication is correct.

Use multiplication to check if the division is correct.

$$68 \div 2 = \underline{34}$$

Check 34×2

$$\underline{} \times \underline{}$$

The division is _____.

① $37 \times 2 = \underline{74}$ ◯

Check

② $98 \div 7 = \underline{13}$ ◯

Check

③ $16 \times 4 = \underline{64}$ ◯

Check

④ $81 \div 3 = \underline{27}$ ◯

Check

⑤ $29 \times 3 = \underline{67}$ ◯

Check

⑥ $72 \div 4 = \underline{18}$ ◯

Check

Do the multiplication and division. Then check your answers.

⑦ $23 \times 2 =$ _____

⑧ $96 \div 6 =$ _____

⑨ $72 \div 2 =$ _____

⑩ $11 \times 9 =$ _____

⑪ $68 \div 4 =$ _____

⑫ $12 \times 8 =$ _____

⑬ $70 \div 5 =$ _____

⑭ $36 \times 2 =$ _____

⑮ $48 \div 4 =$ _____

⑯ $23 \times 5 =$ _____

⑰ $12 \times 7 =$ _____

⑱ $21 \times 3 =$ _____

⑲ $72 \div 6 =$ _____

⑳ $85 \div 5 =$ _____

㉑ $27 \times 2 =$ _____

㉒ $98 \div 7 =$ _____

㉓ $46 \div 2 =$ _____

㉔ $19 \times 5 =$ _____

㉕ $28 \times 3 =$ _____

㉖ $63 \div 3 =$ _____

㉗ $26 \times 4 =$ _____

LEVEL 2 – FURTHER YOUR UNDERSTANDING

Check the answers to the division questions. Put a check mark in the circle if the answer is correct. Show your steps.

Hints

㉘ a. $62 \div 5 =$ ___12R2___ ◯

    Check _____ x _____ = _____

    _____ + _____ = _____

b. $43 \div 7 =$ ___6R5___ ◯

    Check _____

    _____

c. $56 \div 3 =$ ___18R2___ ◯

    Check _____

    _____

Follow the steps below to check answers that have remainders.

❶ Multiply the quotient and the divisor.

❷ Add the remainder to the product. If the sum is the same as the dividend, the answer is correct.

e.g. $34 \div 5 = 6R4$?

    Check $6 \times 5 = 30$

           $30 + 4 = 34$

So, the division is correct.

d. $92 \div 7 =$ ___13R1___ ◯

    Check _____

    _____

e. $83 \div 6 =$ ___13R5___ ◯

    Check _____

    _____

f. $41 \div 9 =$ ___4R5___ ◯

    Check _____

    _____

g. $38 \div 7 =$ ___5R4___ ◯

    Check _____

    _____

h. $76 \div 5 =$ ___15R1___ ◯

    Check _____

    _____

i. $69 \div 8 =$ ___8R5___ ◯

    Check _____

    _____

j. $57 \div 4 =$ ___14R2___ ◯

    Check _____

    _____

k. $70 \div 6 =$ ___11R5___ ◯

    Check _____

    _____

Do the division. Then check your answers using multiplication and addition. Show your steps.

㉙

$6\overline{)75}$

Check

_____

_____

㉚

$2\overline{)29}$

Check

_____

_____

㉛

$3\overline{)56}$

Check

_____

_____

Solve the problems and check your answers.

㉜ Jason has 3 bags of 24 marbles. How many marbles does he have in all?

Check

_____ marbles

㉝ Ethan divides 68 candies equally among his 4 uncles. How many candies does each uncle get?

Check

_____ candies

㉞ A farmer puts 38 eggs into 3 cartons and has some left over. How many eggs are in each carton and how many are left over?

Check

_____ eggs in each carton with _____ left

5 Fractions

- describing and comparing fractions of sets of objects

Fractions can be used to describe parts of a whole as well as parts of a set of objects.

Part of a whole

 $\frac{1}{2}$ shaded

Part of a set

$\frac{1}{2}$ shaded

Example Write a fraction to describe the shaded circles in the set.

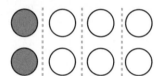

Fraction: $\frac{1}{4}$ ← 1 group shaded
← 4 equal groups

Try It

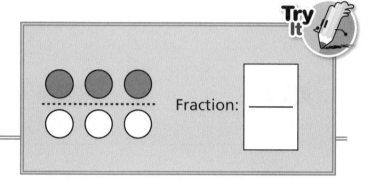

Fraction: ———

Circle the fraction that describes the shaded part of each set.

①

$\frac{1}{4}$ $\frac{1}{3}$

② ●●●● ●●●● ○○○○

$\frac{2}{3}$ $\frac{2}{12}$

③

$\frac{2}{8}$ $\frac{2}{4}$

④

$\frac{1}{2}$ $\frac{1}{5}$

⑤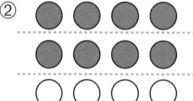

$\frac{4}{6}$ $\frac{8}{6}$

⑥

$\frac{3}{4}$ $\frac{3}{9}$

Write a fraction to describe the shaded part of each set.

⑦

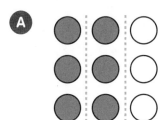

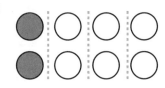

Fraction

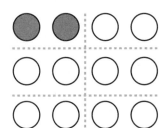

Ⓐ _____

Ⓑ _____

Ⓒ _____

Ⓓ _____

Ⓔ _____

Ⓕ _____

Colour to show each fraction.

⑧ $\frac{2}{7}$

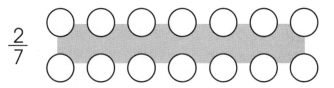

!Tips

To find the fraction, draw lines to put each group into the correct number of parts first.

⑨ $\frac{1}{3}$

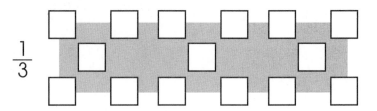

⑩ $\frac{3}{5}$

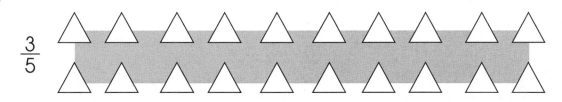

Colour to show each fraction.

⑪
$\frac{1}{4}$: red apples

$\frac{3}{4}$: green apples

⑫
$\frac{2}{3}$: red peppers

$\frac{1}{3}$: yellow peppers

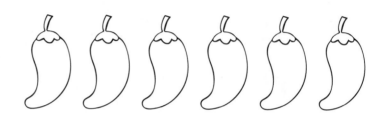

⑬
$\frac{2}{5}$: green leaves

$\frac{3}{5}$: yellow leaves

Compare the fractions. Put ">" or "<" in the circles.

⑭ $\frac{3}{5}$ ◯ $\frac{2}{5}$

⑮ $\frac{1}{6}$ ◯ $\frac{2}{6}$

⑯ $\frac{6}{8}$ ◯ $\frac{5}{8}$

⑰ $\frac{4}{3}$ ◯ $\frac{1}{3}$

⑱ $\frac{2}{7}$ ◯ $\frac{5}{7}$

⑲ $\frac{8}{5}$ ◯ $\frac{4}{5}$

⑳ $\frac{3}{4}$ ◯ $\frac{4}{4}$

㉑ $\frac{9}{10}$ ◯ $\frac{2}{10}$

㉒ $\frac{5}{9}$ ◯ $\frac{6}{9}$

㉓ $\frac{6}{6}$ ◯ $\frac{0}{6}$

㉔ $\frac{1}{8}$ ◯ $\frac{3}{8}$

㉕ $\frac{4}{11}$ ◯ $\frac{5}{11}$

㉖ $\frac{8}{9}$ ◯ $\frac{12}{9}$

㉗ $\frac{9}{7}$ ◯ $\frac{6}{7}$

Hints

Fractions with the same denominator can be compared by their numerators. The fraction that has the greater numerator is greater.

e.g. $\frac{2}{3} > \frac{1}{3}$ ← 2 > 1
   ← same denominator

Put the fractions in order from smallest to greatest.

㉘ $\dfrac{3}{5}$ $\dfrac{5}{5}$ $\dfrac{2}{5}$ $\dfrac{4}{5}$

___ < ___ < ___ < ___

㉙ $\dfrac{1}{8}$ $\dfrac{5}{8}$ $\dfrac{0}{8}$ $\dfrac{9}{8}$

_____

㉚ $\dfrac{3}{10}$ $\dfrac{7}{10}$ $\dfrac{9}{10}$ $\dfrac{4}{10}$

_____

㉛ $\dfrac{2}{9}$ $\dfrac{11}{9}$ $\dfrac{4}{9}$ $\dfrac{1}{9}$

_____

㉜ $\dfrac{7}{8}$ $\dfrac{6}{8}$ $\dfrac{8}{8}$ $\dfrac{2}{8}$

_____

㉝ $\dfrac{8}{7}$ $\dfrac{0}{7}$ $\dfrac{4}{7}$ $\dfrac{1}{7}$

_____

Count forward as specified to complete the number lines. Then draw arrows to locate the fractions.

㉞ Count forward by $\dfrac{1}{4}$'s. Locate $\dfrac{3}{4}$.

㉟ Count forward by $\dfrac{1}{9}$'s. Locate $\dfrac{2}{9}$ and $\dfrac{5}{9}$.

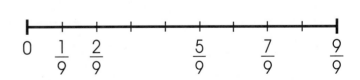

㊱ Count forward by $\dfrac{1}{5}$'s. Locate $\dfrac{1}{5}$ and $\dfrac{6}{5}$.

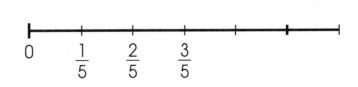

6 Decimals

• adding and subtracting decimals to the tenths

Adding and subtracting decimals is similar to adding and subtracting whole numbers. Use diagrams to help you grasp the concept.

Example Colour to help you do the addition.

e.g.   0.4 + 0.3 = ?

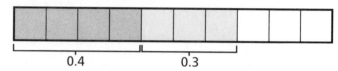

0.4   0.3

0.4 + 0.3 = 0.7 ← 0.7 of the diagram shaded

Try It

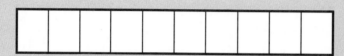

0.5 + 0.1 =

Colour the diagrams to help you do the addition.

①

0.2 + 0.3 = _____

②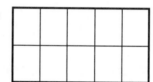

0.4 + 0.4 = _____

Tips

Fill up one rectangle before you start colouring a new one. Each rectangle is one whole.

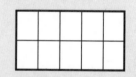

1 whole = 10 tenths

③

0.6 + 0.5 = _____

④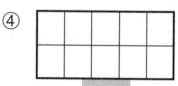

0.3 + 0.9 = _____

⑤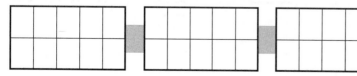

1.3 + 0.6 = _____

⑥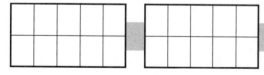

1.8 + 0.7 = _____

Do the addition.

⑦
```
    0.4
+   0.3
```

⑧
```
    1.6
+   0.2
```

⑨
```
    0.7
+   0.4
```

⑩
```
    0.8
+   0.5
```

⑪
```
    1.9
+   0.4
```

⑫
```
    0.5
+   1.8
```

⑬
```
    2.8
+   0.2
```

⑭
```
    1.7
+   1.7
```

⑮
```
    2.3
+   1.8
```

Hints

Add decimals as if they are whole numbers. Then align to add a decimal point to the answer.

e.g.
```
    0 . 3
+   0 . 2
    0 . 5
```
↑
Align to add a decimal point.

LEVEL 2 – FURTHER YOUR UNDERSTANDING

Do the addition. Show your work.

⑯ 0.6 + 0.3 = _____
```
    0.6
+   0.3
```

⑰ 1.1 + 0.4 = _____

⑱ 1.8 + 1.3 = _____

⑲ 0.9 + 2.4 = _____

⑳ 0.5 + 1.7 = _____

㉑ 1.4 + 2.8 = _____

㉒ 0.7 + 3.5 = _____

Hints

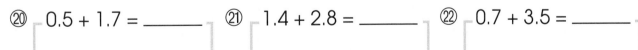

Align the decimal points in the addends before adding.

e.g. 1.2 + 0.3 = ?

```
    1 . 2
+       0 . 3
```
✗

```
    1 . 2
+   0 . 3
```
✓

Use the diagrams to help you do the subtraction.

㉓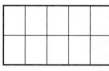

1.8 – 0.3 = _____

㉔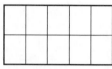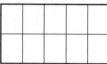

1.5 – 0.2 = _____

㉕

1.2 – 0.5 = _____

㉖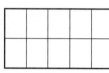

1.8 – 1.3 = _____

㉗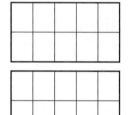

1.7 – 0.8 = _____

㉘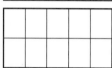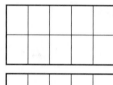

1.4 – 0.6 = _____

Hints

Follow these steps to subtract decimals.

❶ Draw and colour to show the first decimal.

❷ Cross out the second decimal.

❸ The remaining part is the answer.

e.g. 1.6 – 0.5 = ?

1.6 – 0.5 = __1.1__

Do the subtraction.

㉙
```
   1.4
 – 0.3
_____
```

㉚
```
   2.5
 – 1.1
_____
```

㉛
```
   4.7
 – 2.5
_____
```

Tips

Remember to add the decimal point to the answer.

㉜
```
   3.2
 – 1.6
_____
```

㉝
```
   1.3
 – 0.9
_____
```

㉞
```
   2.7
 – 1.8
_____
```

㉟
```
   5.0
 – 3.2
_____
```

Do the subtraction. Show your work.

㊱ 2.6 – 1.2 = _____

㊲ 6.8 – 4.6 = _____

㊳ 5.4 – 2.6 = _____

㊴ 3.6 – 2.5 = _____

㊵ 1.5 – 0.8 = _____

㊶ 6.1 – 5.9 = _____

㊷ 4.3 – 2.4 = _____

㊸ 2.5 – 1.6 = _____

㊹ 3.3 – 2.4 = _____

Find the answers. Show your work.

㊺
A 2.4 + 1.2 = _____ **B** 3.6 – 1.3 = _____

C 3 + 0.5 = _____ **D** 1 – 0.1 = _____

E 5 – 1.3 = _____ **F** 2.7 + 1.4 = _____

G 4 – 1.2 = _____ **H** 3.3 + 2.9 = _____

Tips

Add "0" as a placeholder when needed.

e.g. 2 – 0.7 = ?

placeholder
↓
$$\begin{array}{r} 2.\mathbf{0} \\ -\ 0.7 \\ \hline 1.3 \end{array}$$

7 Money

- representing, adding, and subtracting money amounts up to $100

Read This

To find the money amount of a set of bills and coins, first group the bills and coins of the same kind. Then start counting with the kind of bill or coin that has the highest value.

Example Find the total amount of money.

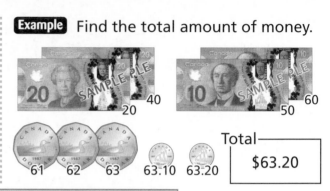

20 → 40
20
10 → 60
50
61   62   63   63.10   63.20

Total— $63.20

Try It

Total—

Find how much money each child has.

①

$

②

③

Using the fewest bills and coins, draw the symbols to show the cost of each item.

Start with the kind of bill with the highest value first. Then do the same for the coins.

④ **Symbols**

$50	$20	$10	$5

$2 $1   25¢   10¢   5¢

a. **$14.30**

b. **$50.25**

c.  **$78.75**

d. **$26.80**

LEVEL 2 – FURTHER YOUR UNDERSTANDING

Add and subtract the money amounts.

⑤
dollar	cent
3	25
+ 2	10

Sum

⑥
dollar	cent
2	30
– 1	15

Difference

Hints

To add or subtract money amounts, line up the dollars and cents first.

e.g.
dollar	cent
2	50
+ 1	65

4 ₃ 1̶1̶5̶ (100)+ 15

Trade 100¢ for $1.

Sum: **$4.15**

⑦
dollar	cent
5	45
+ 2	65

Sum

⑧
dollar	cent
7	10
– 1	35

Difference

dollar	cent
6 7̶	4̶5̶ 145	Trade $1 for 100¢.
– 1	80
5̶	65

Difference: **$5.65**

Find the sum and the difference for each pair of money amounts.

⑨   **$6.25 $4.50**

Sum:

⑩   **$10.70 $1.35**

Sum:

⑪   **$8 $1.50**

Sum:

Difference:

Difference:

Difference:

Look at the costs of the toys. Find the answers.

⑫ Find the total costs.

a. and

b. and

 $11.90

 $20.15

 $10.95

⑬ Find the differences in costs.

a.  and

b.  and

 $22.50

⑭

This is all I have with me. How much change will I get if I buy...

a. a doll?

b. a toy car?

LEVEL 2 – FURTHER YOUR UNDERSTANDING

8 Area

• finding the areas of polygons in square centimetres

To find the area of a shape on a centimetre grid, count the number of squares the shape covers. You can number each square that you count to make sure you do not count it twice.

Example Find the area of the square.

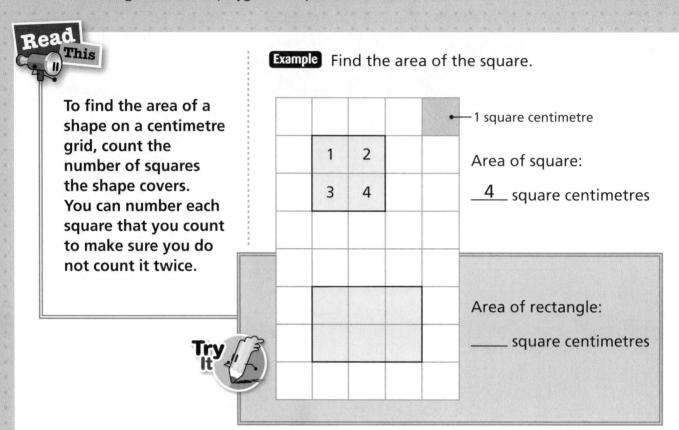

— 1 square centimetre

Area of square:

__4__ square centimetres

Area of rectangle:

_____ square centimetres

Try It

Find the area of the shape on each centimetre grid.

①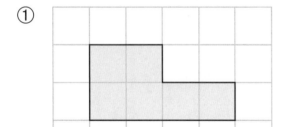

_____ square centimetres

②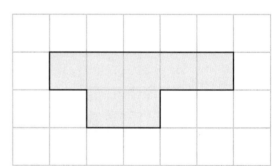

_____ square centimetres

③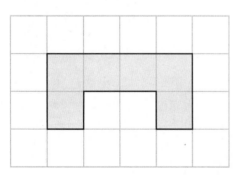

_____ square centimetres

④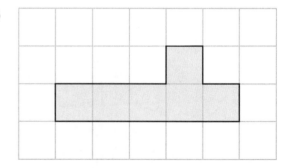

_____ square centimetres

Find the areas of the shapes on the centimetre grid. Then answer the questions.

⑤

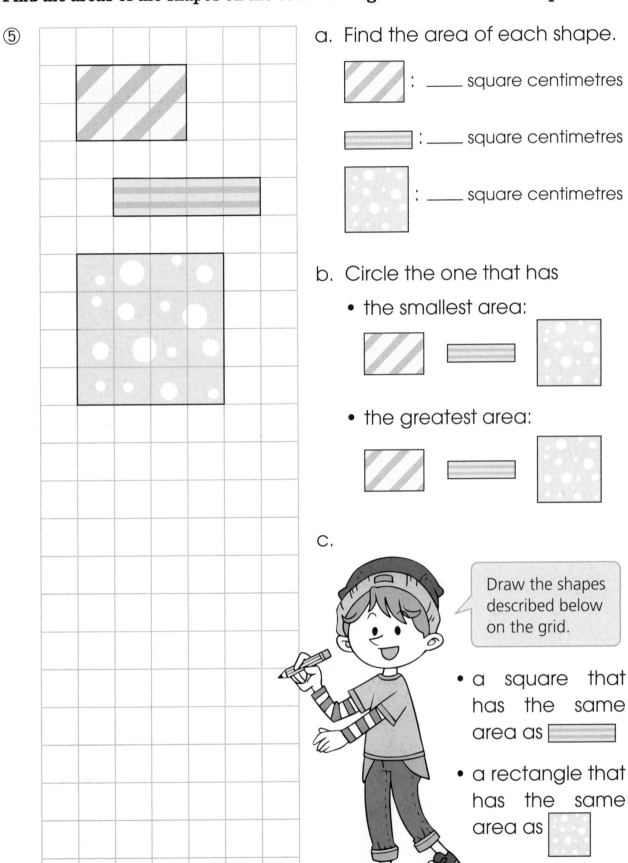

a. Find the area of each shape.

: ＿＿ square centimetres

: ＿＿ square centimetres

: ＿＿ square centimetres

b. Circle the one that has

- the smallest area:

- the greatest area:

c.

Draw the shapes described below on the grid.

- a square that has the same area as

- a rectangle that has the same area as

Karen drew some shapes on the centimetre grid. Find and record the areas of the shapes. Then draw the shape she describes.

⑥

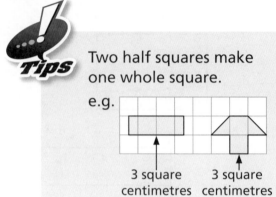

Two half squares make one whole square.

e.g.

3 square centimetres   3 square centimetres

a.   **Area**

[rectangle] : _____ square centimetres

[house/pentagon] : _____ square centimetres

[diamond] : _____ square centimetres

[cross shape] : _____ square centimetres

[trough shape] : _____ square centimetres

b. Colour the shapes with the same area yellow.

c. Colour the shape that has the greatest area blue.

Karen

d. Draw an isosceles right triangle with an area of 18 square centimetres.

Calculate to find the area of each shape.

⑦

Area:

_____ X _____
length   width

= _____ (square centimetres)

Another way to find the areas of rectangles and squares is by multiplying the length and width of the shape.

e.g.

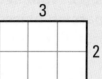

⑧

Area:

_____ X _____
length   width

= _____ (square centimetres)

Area: 3 x 2
     = 6 (square centimetres)

⑨ Count to find the area of each shape and compare it with the area you calculated. Are they the same? _____

Measure the length and width of each shape using a ruler. Then calculate to find the area.

⑩

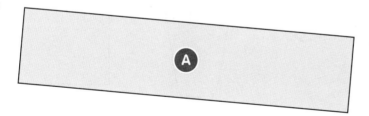

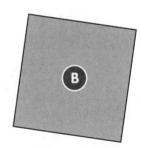

Areas

Ⓐ _____ square centimetres

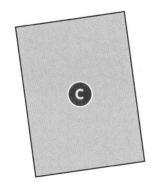

Ⓑ _____

Ⓒ _____

9 Capacity and Volume

• understanding and describing the capacity and the volume

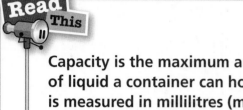
Read This

Capacity is the maximum amount of liquid a container can hold. It is measured in millilitres (mL) and litres (L). Volume is the amount of space an object takes up. It is measured in cubic centimetres.

Example Circle the better measuring unit for the capacity of the object.

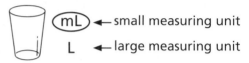

mL ← small measuring unit

L ← large measuring unit

Try It

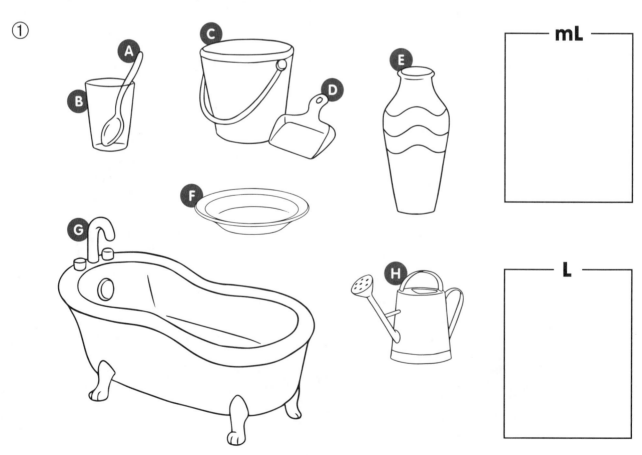

mL

L

Write the letters in the boxes to match the objects with the appropriate units of capacity.

①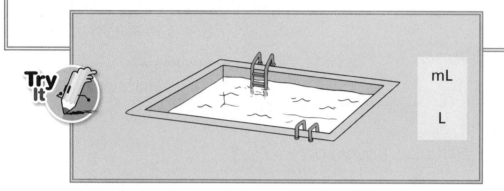

mL

L

Circle the better estimate of each capacity.

②  30 mL
300 mL

③  1000 mL
100 mL

 5 mL

2 L

④  5 L
50 L

⑤  3 L
300 L

Do the conversions.

⑥ 3 L = _____ mL

6 L = _____ mL

4 L = _____ mL

10 L = _____ mL

9 L = _____ mL

⑦ 7000 mL = _____ L

8000 mL = _____ L

5000 mL = _____ L

20 000 mL = _____ L

12 000 mL = _____ L

Hints

1 L = 1000 mL

Look at the capacity of each mug. Write how many of each mug of water are needed to fill the given jugs.

⑧  100 mL

250 mL

500 mL

LEVEL 2 – FURTHER YOUR UNDERSTANDING

Write the volume of each structure in cubic centimetres.

⑨ 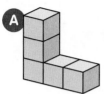 A   B   C

Hints

A cube that measures 1 cm by 1 cm by 1 cm has a volume of 1 cubic centimetre.

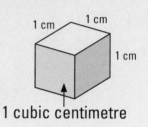

1 cubic centimetre

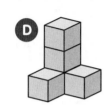 D   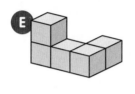 E   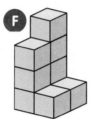 F

Volume

A _____ cubic centimetres

B _____

C _____

D _____

E _____

F _____

Trace to complete each structure and find its volume. Then draw another structure with the same volume.

⑩

_____ cubic centimetres

⑪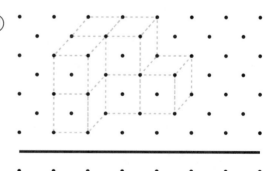

_____ cubic centimetres

Read each question. Check to show whether it is about capacity or volume.

⑫

	Capacity	Volume
a. Which couch takes up more space?	○	○
b. Which bottle can hold more liquid?	○	○
c. Which bucket can I put more water in?	○	○
d. Which cake is larger?	○	○
e. Which teapot holds more tea?	○	○
f. Which lamp takes up more room?	○	○

Circle the correct answers to complete what each child says.

⑬

My backpack can hold a lot. It has a capacity of **2 / 20** L. I always put a box of crayons in it which is about **20 / 240** cubic centimetres.

Tips Remember that mL and L are for capacity. Cubic centimetres are for volume.

⑭

My mom packs my lunch every day. She always packs my favourite juice boxes, which hold 250 **mL / L** of apple juice. There is always a stick of celery too, which is about **15 / 50** cubic centimetres. Thanks, Mom!

10 Time

- finding elapsed times

Read This

Elapsed time is the amount of time between the beginning of an event and its end.

Example Find the elapsed time from Tuesday to Friday.

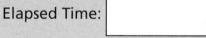

Tuesday Wednesday Thursday Friday
1 day 2 days 3 days

Elapsed time: **3 days**

Find the elapsed times.

Try It

Find the elapsed time from March to July.

Elapsed Time: _____

① Monday → Saturday

_____

② Friday → Monday

_____

③ January → May

_____

④ March → November

_____

⑤ 2014 → 2019

_____

⑥ 2018 → 2023

_____

⑦ Saturday → Tuesday

_____

⑧ February → November

_____

⑨ Wednesday → Sunday

_____

⑩ July → May

_____

⑪ Thursday → Sunday

_____

⑫ This project started in 2016 and ended in 2018.

_____

⑬ The park opens in June and closes in October.

_____

Answer the questions with the help of the calendars.

	APRIL					
S	M	T	W	T	F	S
	1	2	3	4	5	6
7	8	9	10	11	12	13
14	15	16	17	18	19	20
21	22	23	24	25	26	27
28	29	30				

	MAY					
S	M	T	W	T	F	S
			1	2	3	4
5	6	7	8	9	10	11
12	13	14	15	16	17	18
19	20	21	22	23	24	25
26	27	28	29	30	31	

	JUNE					
S	M	T	W	T	F	S
						1
2	3	4	5	6	7	8
9	10	11	12	13	14	15
16	17	18	19	20	21	22
23	24	25	26	27	28	29
30						

⑭ Find the elapsed times.

a. April 10 to April 17 _____

b. April 29 to May 2 _____

c. May 31 to June 6 _____

d. April 29 to June 1 _____

⑮ Find the end dates of the trips.

a. started on April 7 and lasted for 10 days _____

b. started on April 28 and lasted for 5 days _____

c. started on May 3 and lasted for 2 weeks _____

d. started on May 25 and lasted for 3 weeks _____

⑯ Find the start dates.

a.  I spent 12 days preparing the garden. It was ready on April 15. _____

b.  This flower took 6 weeks to bloom. It bloomed on May 19. _____

c. I finished tiling the backyard on June 20. It took 3 days. _____

Find the elapsed times in minutes.

⑰ from 4:30 to 4:50

_____

⑱ from 12:15 to 12:50

_____

⑲ from 1:05 to 1:20

_____

⑳ from 3:20 to 3:40

_____

㉑ from 10:10 to 10:45

_____

㉒ from 11:05 to 11:40

_____

Find the elapsed times with the help of the clock.

㉓

Draw the times to help find the answers.

a. from 1:40 to 2:20   _____

b. from 6:45 to 7:20   _____

c. from 11:55 to 12:20   _____

d. from 8:15 to 9:05   _____

Hints

Steps to find the elapsed time in minutes:

❶ Check the minute hand of the start time.

❷ Start counting by 5's from there until you reach the minute hand of the end time.

e.g. 3:50 to 4:10

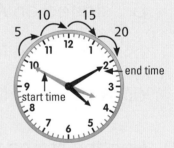

Elapsed time: 20 minutes

Read the clocks. Find the elapsed times in hours and minutes.

㉔ Start   ㉕ Start

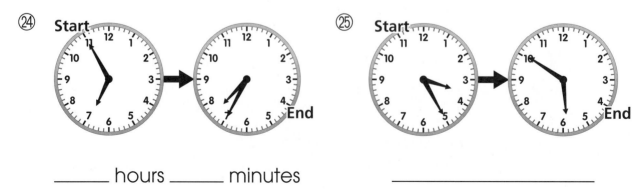

_____ hours _____ minutes   _____

Use the timeline of Sue's morning schedule and read what Sue says to answer the questions.

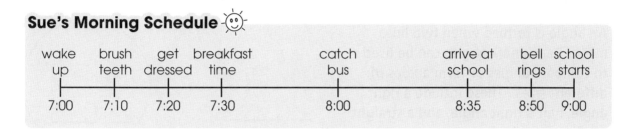

Sue's Morning Schedule ☺

| wake up | brush teeth | get dressed | breakfast time | | catch bus | | arrive at school | bell rings | school starts |
| 7:00 | 7:10 | 7:20 | 7:30 | | 8:00 | | 8:35 | 8:50 | 9:00 |

㉖ How much time does Sue have to

a. brush her teeth? _____

b. get dressed? _____

c. eat breakfast? _____

㉗ How long is her bus ride to school? _____

㉘ Will she be late for school if the bus comes at 8:10? _____

㉙ How many minutes before school starts does the bell ring? _____

㉚

> My first class is Math and it is 50 minutes long. The next class is English, which is also 50 minutes long. After the English class, we have a 15-minute recess.

Complete the timeline of Sue's schedule.

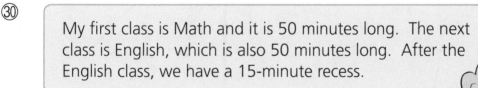

Math class

| 9:00 | | | 11:00 |

㉛ Sue finishes school at 2:40. How long is her school day?

_____

11 Angles

- identifying benchmark angles and their measures

Read This

An angle is formed when two lines meet. Benchmark angles can be used to compare angles or form angles of different sizes. These include a right angle, half a right angle, and a straight angle.

Example Circle the right angle.

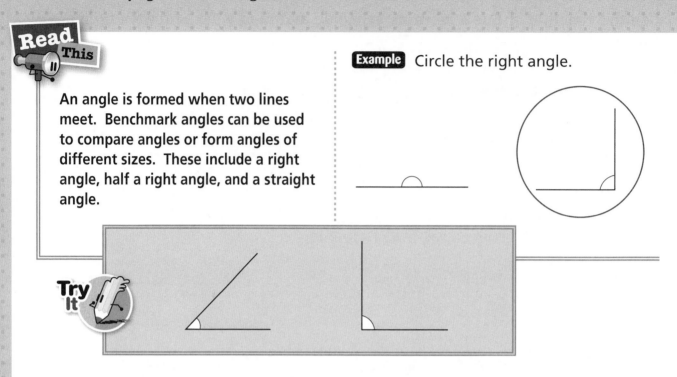

Try It

Trace the square below onto a piece of paper. Then cut it out and fold it to help identify benchmark angles. Colour each angle the correct colour.

①

RED — right angle

BLUE — half a right angle

GREEN — straight angle

Trace, cut, and fold.

half a right angle

right angle

straight angle

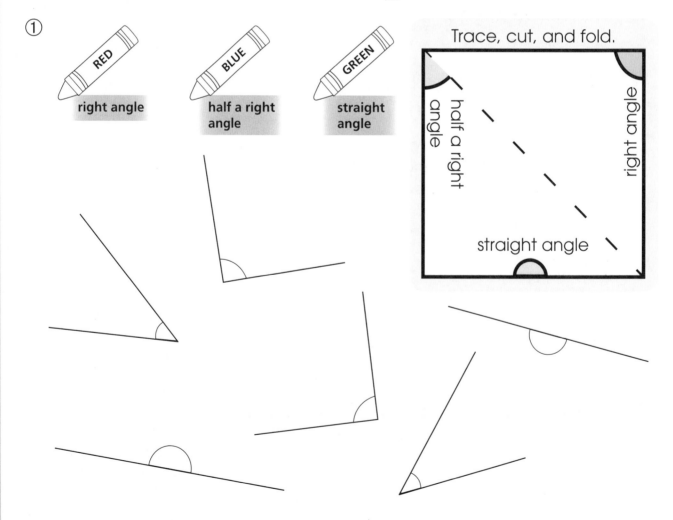

Look at the pictures. Write the names of the benchmark angles. Then fill in the blanks with "greater" or "smaller".

②

Angles

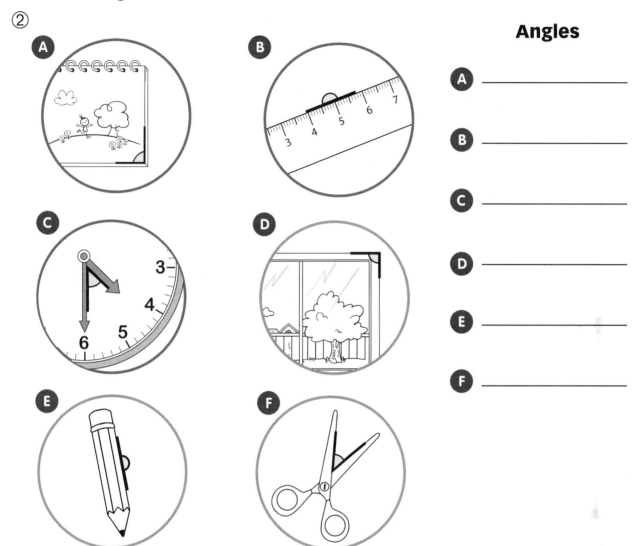

A _____

B _____

C _____

D _____

E _____

F _____

③ The angle that the hour hand and the minute hand make in **C** is _____ than a right angle.

④

The corner of my sketch book is _____ than a straight angle but _____ than half a right angle.

Write the measure of each angle.

Hints

The size of an angle is measured in degrees (°). The measures of the benchmark angles are shown below.

180° straight angle

90° right angle

45° half a right angle

⑤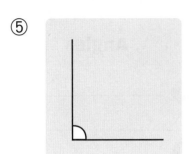

_____ °

⑥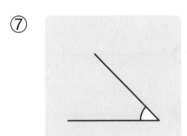

_____

⑦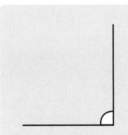

_____

⑧

_____

⑨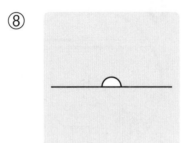

_____

⑩

_____

⑪

_____

⑫

_____

⑬

_____

⑭

_____

Circle the angles that fit each description.

⑮ smaller than a right angle

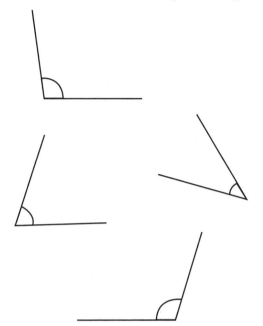

⑯ between half a right angle and a right angle

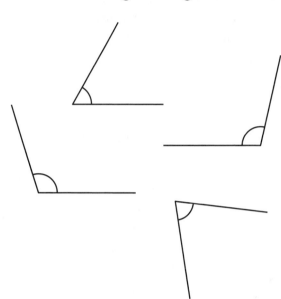

Help each child sketch the angle as described. Then answer the question.

⑰

My angle is smaller than half a right angle.

My angle is between the sizes of a right angle and a straight angle.

My angle is between the sizes of half a right angle and a right angle.

⑱ Whose angle is the smallest? Whose angle is the largest? Draw the faces.

smallest	largest

12 Solids

- relating solids to their nets and skeletons

A net is a flat shape that can be folded to make a solid. A skeleton is the "frame" of a solid.

e.g.

net   skeleton

Example Circle the net of the solid.

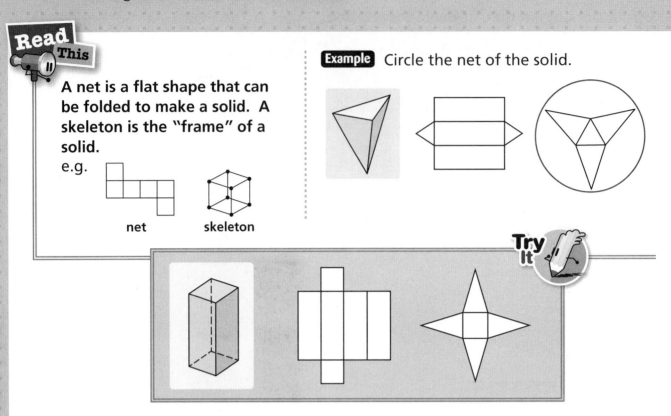

Match the solids with their nets. Write the letters.

①

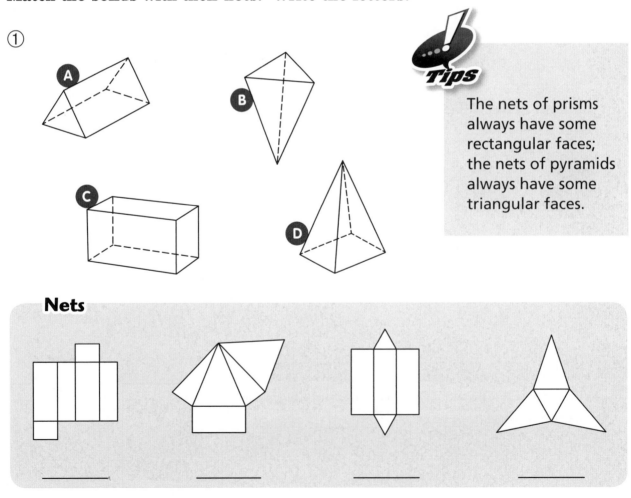

Tips

The nets of prisms always have some rectangular faces; the nets of pyramids always have some triangular faces.

Nets

_____   _____   _____   _____

Circle the correct net for each solid.

②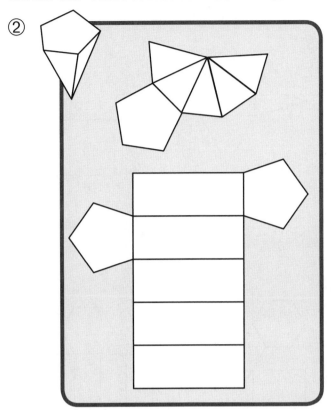

③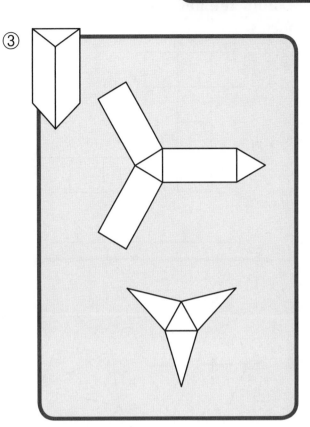

Trace the nets below onto a sheet of paper. Cut them out and fold them along the dotted lines. Check the net that makes a solid and name the solid.

④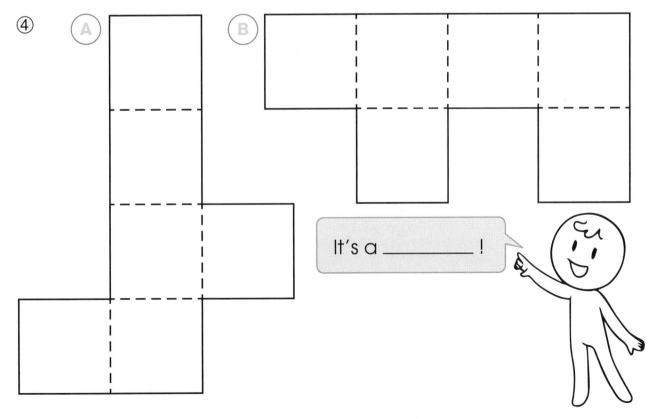

It's a _____ !

Colour the net that can form a solid in each pair. Then name the solid the net forms.

⑤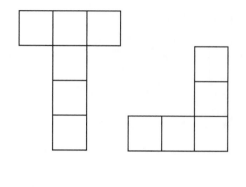

_____

⑥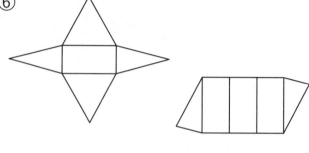

_____

⑦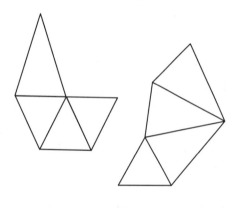

_____

⑧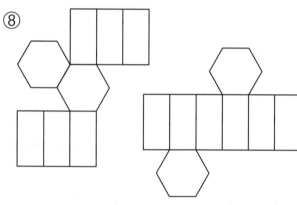

_____

Match the solids with their skeletons. Write the letters.

⑨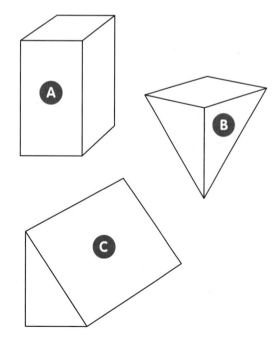

Skeletons

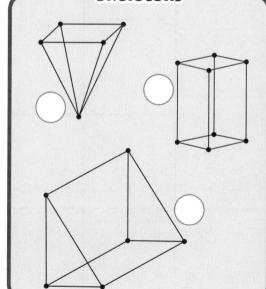

Complete the skeleton of each solid.

⑩ rectangular prism ⑪ hexagonal pyramid ⑫ pentagonal prism

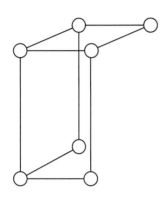 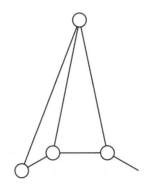 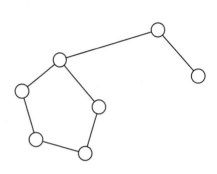

Alicia wants to make some solids using sticks and clay. Name the solid that each set of sticks and clay makes and then sketch the skeleton.

⑬

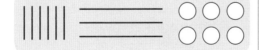

⑮

I have 5 short sticks, 5 long sticks, and 6 balls of clay.

⑭

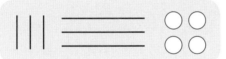

13 Patterning

• describing and extending number patterns and geometric patterns

Read This

Each number in a pattern is called a term. Find the relationship between the terms to determine the pattern rule.

Example Check the number pattern that follows the given pattern rule.

Start at 5. Add 2 each time.

○ 5, 7, 10, 14, 19 ← does not add 2 each time

✓ 5, 7, 9, 11, 13

Try It

Start at 20. Subtract 3 each time.

Ⓐ 20, 17, 14, 11, 8

Ⓑ 20, 23, 26, 29, 32

Complete the number patterns with the given pattern rules.

① Start at 1. Add 4 each time.

1, 5, 9, 13, _____, _____, _____, _____

② Start at 15. Subtract 2 each time.

15, 13, 11, 9, _____, _____, _____, _____

③ Start at 10. Add 3. Then subtract 1.

10, 13, 12, 15, 14, _____, _____, _____, _____

④ Start at 12. Subtract 3. Then add 2.

12, 9, 11, 8, 10, _____, _____, _____, _____

⑤

Start at 9. Subtract 4. Then multiply by 2.

9, 5, 10, 6, 12, _____, _____, _____

Start at 4. Multiply by 2. Then subtract 3.

4, 8, 5, 10, 7, _____, _____, _____

Write the patterns according to the given pattern rules.

⑥　Start at 10.　Add 3.　Then subtract 1.

　　10, _____ , _____ , _____ , _____

⑦　Start at 30.　Subtract 10.　Then add 5.

　　_____ , _____ , _____ , _____ , _____

⑧　Start at 6.　Multiply by 2.　Then subtract 5.

　　_____ , _____ , _____ , _____ , _____

⑨　Start at 7.　Subtract 3.　Then add 2.

　　_____ , _____ , _____ , _____ , _____

Complete each number pattern.　Then write its pattern rule.

Tips　There may be more than one kind of operation in a pattern.

⑩　**1　4　7　10**　_____　_____　_____

　　Pattern Rule　Start at _____ . Add _____ each time.

⑪　**3　4　6　7　9**　_____　_____　_____

　　Pattern Rule　Start at _____ . Add _____ . Then add _____ .

⑫　**30　25　26　21　22**　_____　_____　_____

　　Pattern Rule　_____

⑬　**3　6　5　10　9**　_____　_____　_____

　　Pattern Rule　_____

⑭　**2　4　8　10　20**　_____　_____　_____

　　Pattern Rule　_____

Fill in the missing terms.

⑮ 13   10   11   8   _____   _____   7   4   _____

⑯ 7   14   9   18   _____   _____   21   42   _____

⑰ 1   3   2   6   _____   15   _____   _____

⑱ 5   3   9   _____   21   19   _____   _____

Answer the questions about the patterns in the tables.

Each number in a pattern is called a term. Term numbers show the order of the terms.

⑲ **Pattern A**

Term Number	Term
1	4
2	3
3	6
4	5
5	10

a. Check the correct pattern rule.

Ⓐ Start at 4. Subtract 1. Then multiply by 2.

Ⓑ Start at 4. Subtract 1 each time.

b. Find the terms.

• 6th term: _____

• 8th term: _____

• 9th term: _____

⑳ **Pattern B**

Term Number	Term
1	3
2	6
3	4
4	8
5	6

a. Write the pattern rule.

_____

_____

b. Find the terms.

• 6th term: _____

• 7th term: _____

• 9th term: _____

• 10th term: _____

Look at the geometric patterns and complete the tables. Then answer the questions about the patterns.

㉑

  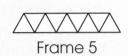

Frame 1   Frame 2   Frame 3   Frame 4   Frame 5

a.

Frame Number	Number of Triangles
1	
2	
3	
4	
5	

b. Write the pattern rule.

_____

c. How many triangles are there in

• Frame 6? _____

• Frame 8? _____

• Frame 10? _____

㉒

Frame 1   Frame 2   Frame 3   Frame 4   Frame 5

I used sticks to make the pattern above.

a.

Frame Number	1	2	3	4	5
Number of Sticks					

b. Write the pattern rule.

_____

c. How many sticks are there in

• Frame 7? _____

• Frame 9? _____

• Frame 10? _____

14 Simple Equations

• solving simple equations

You may make use of the related facts in a fact family to find the unknown value in an equation.

A fact family involves either

• addition and subtraction facts, or
• multiplication and division facts.

Example Find the missing number by making use of the fact family of 5, 10, and 15.

$10 + ? = 15$

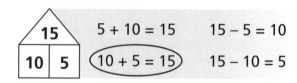

15		
10	5	

$5 + 10 = 15$ $15 - 5 = 10$
$(10 + 5 = 15)$ $15 - 10 = 5$

So, the missing number is 5.

Try It

Fill in the missing numbers in the equations.

$\boxed{} - 5 = 10$ $5 + \boxed{} = 15$

Write the related facts for each fact family. Then find the missing numbers.

①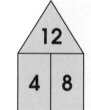

12	
4	8

$4 + \boxed{} = 12$ | $12 - \boxed{} = 8$

②

15	
3	5

$5 \times \boxed{} = 15$ | $15 \div \boxed{} = 3$

③

20	
4	5

$20 \div \boxed{} = 4$ | $\boxed{} \times 4 = 20$

④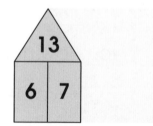

13	
6	7

$\boxed{} - 6 = 7$ | $\boxed{} + 7 = 13$

Solve to show the inverse relationships.

⑤ **3 × 6 = 18**

Inverse:

18 ÷ 6 = _____

18 ÷ 3 = _____

⑥ **48 ÷ 6 = 8**

Inverse:

6 × 8 = _____

8 × 6 = _____

⑦ **8 + 7 = 15**

Inverse:

_____

_____

⑧ **16 – 3 = 13**

Inverse:

_____

_____

⑨ **5 × 9 = 45**

Inverse:

_____

_____

⑩ **63 ÷ 7 = 9**

Inverse:

_____

_____

⑪ **21 – 4 = 17**

Inverse:

_____

_____

⑫ **28 ÷ 7 = 4**

Inverse:

_____

_____

⑬ **3 × 7 = 21**

Inverse:

_____

_____

Use inverse relationships to find the missing numbers.

⑭ 8 × ▢ = 24

⑮ 35 ÷ ▢ = 5

⑯ 14 – ▢ = 2

⑰ ▢ + 6 = 21

⑱ 9 ÷ ▢ = 3

⑲ ▢ × 8 = 56

⑳ 36 – ▢ = 20

㉑ 15 + ▢ = 17

㉒ ▢ × 5 = 20

㉓ 27 ÷ ▢ = 9

㉔ 16 – ▢ = 3

㉕ ▢ + 4 = 19

Hints

Knowing the inverse relationships can help you find the missing number in an equation.

e.g.

$$27 ÷ ? = 3$$

Think: 3 × 9 = 27

So, the missing number is 9.

Check Leo's answers. Put a check mark in the circle if the answer is correct; otherwise, put a cross and write the correct answer. Then fill in the blank.

 26

Math Quiz

Name: __Leo C.__

Find the missing numbers.

1. $18 + \boxed{4} = 21$ ◯

2. $6 \times \boxed{7} = 42$ ◯

3. $\boxed{21} - 2 = 18$ ◯

4. $3 + \boxed{14} = 17$ ◯

5. $14 \div \boxed{9} = 2$ ◯

6. $8 \times \boxed{4} = 32$ ◯

7. $8 + \boxed{16} = 24$ ◯

8. $20 - \boxed{12} = 8$ ◯

9. $3 \times \boxed{7} = 21$ ◯

10. $\boxed{36} \div 4 = 9$ ◯

11. $5 + \boxed{3} = 15$ ◯

12. $16 - \boxed{9} = 7$ ◯

13. $72 \div \boxed{8} = 9$ ◯

14. $\boxed{3} \times 6 = 18$ ◯

I have _____ correct answers!

Find the missing number in each equation using any method. Then write the letters of the variables to find out what the teacher says.

㉗ $16 - T = 10$

$T =$ _____

㉘ $17 + H = 38$

$H =$ _____

㉙ $19 - M = 5$

$M =$ _____

㉚ $D + 8 = 40$

$D =$ _____

㉛ $T - 13 = 39$

$T =$ _____

㉜ $S \div 7 = 7$

$S =$ _____

㉝ $C \times 3 = 54$

$C =$ _____

㉞ $14 \times A = 70$

$A =$ _____

㉟ $M \div 4 = 16$

$M =$ _____

㊱ $32 \div E = 8$

$E =$ _____

㊲ $I - 12 = 24$

$I =$ _____

㊳ $8 \times J = 16$

$J =$ _____

㊴ $A + 29 = 40$

$A =$ _____

㊵ $35 \div Y = 5$

$Y =$ _____

The only way to learn mathematics is to do

| | | | | | | | | | | ! |

64 11 6 21 4 14 5 52 36 18 49

Graphs

• using stem-and-leaf plots and reading graphs

A stem-and-leaf plot is a tool that helps organize a set of data. Each number in a data set is split into two parts: the "stem" (the leading digit) and the "leaf" (the last digit).

Example Organize the data into the stem-and-leaf plot.

28	16	24
15	21	19
12	33	21
20	30	31

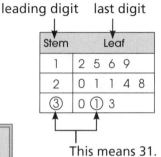

leading digit   last digit

Stem	Leaf
1	2 5 6 9
2	0 1 1 4 8
③	0 ① 3

This means 31.

 Try It

Find the median and the mode of the set of data.

Median: _____   Mode: _____

Read the stem-and-leaf plots. Then find the answers.

①
Stem	Leaf
1	4 6
2	0 1 2 3 9
3	0 1 1 1 2 5

Median: _____

Mode: _____

②
Stem	Leaf
2	1 4 4 6
3	1 5 5 5 7 9
4	0 1 3 9 9

Median: _____

Mode: _____

③
Stem	Leaf
1	3 4 5 6 9
2	0 1 4 6 8
3	0 1 7 9
4	1 3 6 6 7 8

Median: _____

Mode: _____

④
Stem	Leaf
3	0 1 2 2 5 9
4	1 1 8 8 8 9
5	1 1 1 3 4 6
6	0 9

Median: _____

Mode: _____

Match each set of data with the correct stem-and-leaf plot. Then find the answers.

A
89 61 50 52 62 84 68
89 88 73 89 74 52 55 73

B
62 42 58 35 40 59
63 31 62 42 32 42

C
54 40 51 45 50 41 51
63 56 46 60 63 59 62 63

D
51 61 71 60 65 52
78 54 62 72 56

⑤

Stem	Leaf
5	1 2 4 6
6	0 1 2 5
7	1 2 8

Stem	Leaf
4	0 1 5 6
5	0 1 1 4 6 9
6	0 2 3 3 3

Stem	Leaf
5	0 2 2 5
6	1 2 8
7	3 3 4
8	4 8 9 9 9

Stem	Leaf
3	1 2 5
4	0 2 2 2
5	8 9
6	2 2 3

Which data set has

a. 40 as its smallest value? _____

b. 78 as its greatest value? _____

c. a median of 54? _____

d. a median of 61? _____

e. a mode of 89? _____

f. no mode? _____

g. the same median and mode? _____

h. the most 62s? _____

i. the fewest values in the 50s? _____

j. no values ending in 8? _____

⑥ Describe one advantage of organizing a set of data in a stem-and-leaf plot.

_____

_____

Read the double bar graph and answer the questions.

⑦ The students in Mrs. Field's class voted on their favourite food items for lunch.

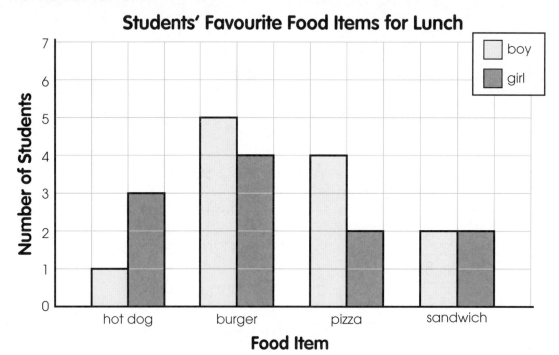

Students' Favourite Food Items for Lunch

a. Which food item is more popular for girls than for boys? _____

b. How many more boys prefer burgers than pizza? _____

c. How many more boys than girls prefer pizza? _____

d. How many students chose hot dogs? _____

e. How many more students chose burgers than hot dogs? _____

f. How many students are boys? _____

g.

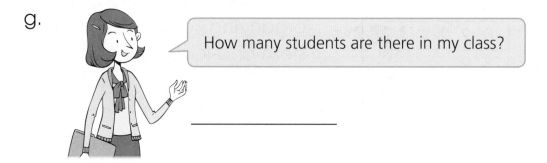

How many students are there in my class?

_____

Leonard recorded the ages of the librarians in his town. Check the stem-and-leaf plot that the bar graph represents. Then answer the questions.

⑧

Stem	Leaf
2	2 8
3	0 1 2 4 9
4	5 6 6 6
5	1 1 2 3

A

Stem	Leaf
2	3 3
3	0 1 1 4 5
4	2 3 4 9 9
5	6 6 7

B

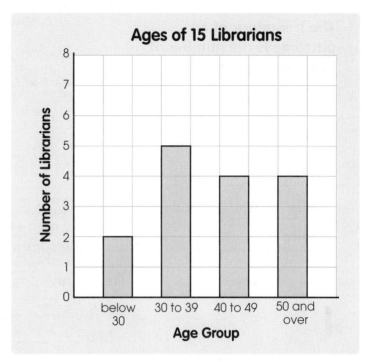

Ages of 15 Librarians

Number of Librarians (vertical axis, 0 to 8)

Age Group (horizontal axis): below 30, 30 to 39, 40 to 49, 50 and over

a. What is the range of the set of data?

_____ years

b. What are the median and mode ages of the librarians?

• median: _____ years old

• mode: _____

c. Which age group has the most librarians?

_____

d. Which age group has the fewest librarians?

_____

Hints

A range is the difference between the greatest and smallest numbers in a group of numbers or a set of data.

e.g.

26   12   34   3   29
          ↑   ↑
     greatest   smallest

34 − 3 = 31

So, the range of the data set is 31.

16 Probability

- finding the frequency of an outcome

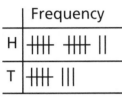

The frequency of an outcome is the number of times it occurs when an experiment is conducted repeatedly.

e.g. Flip a coin 20 times.

	Frequency
H	ⵌ ⵌ ‖
T	ⵌ ‖‖

Example Predict how many times you will get each colour if the spinner is spun 10 times.

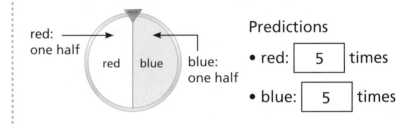

red: one half

red   blue

blue: one half

Predictions

- red: | 5 | times

- blue: | 5 | times

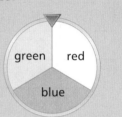

Predict how many times you will get each colour if the spinner is spun 12 times.

Predictions

- red: _____ times

- blue: _____ times

- green: _____ times

For each spinner, predict how many times the parts will be spun based on the given number of spins.

①

a. **12 spins**

 : _____ times   : _____

b. **20 spins**

 : _____   : _____

②

a. **8 spins**

 : _____   : _____

b. **40 spins**

 : _____   : _____

Predict the frequency of each outcome in the scenarios.

 ③

a. flipping the coin 10 times

  • heads: _____ • tails: _____

b. flipping the coin 20 times

  • heads: _____ • tails: _____

 ④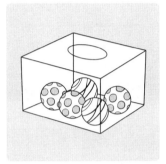

a. picking a ball 10 times

  •

b. picking a ball 15 times

  •

⑤

a. rolling the dice 12 times

  •**1**: _____ •**4**: _____

b. rolling the dice 30 times

  •**2**: _____ •**6**: _____

 ⑥

a. picking a card 10 times

  • ♡: _____ • ☆: _____
  • ☽: _____ • ☀: _____

b. picking a card 30 times

  • ♡: _____ • ☆: _____
  • ☽: _____ • ☀: _____

See the spinner below and determine which child made better predictions for the frequencies of the outcomes. Then answer the questions.

⑦   a.   The spinner shown is spun 60 times.

◯ **Jane's Predictions**

Colour	red	blue	green
Frequency	14	14	32

◯ **Kate's Predictions**

Colour	red	blue	green
Frequency	19	11	30

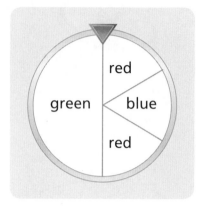

b.   If the spinner is spun 120 times, predict the frequency of each outcome.

• red: _____   • blue: _____   • green: _____

For each scenario, check the most reasonable set of predicted frequencies.

⑧   A card is drawn 50 times.

Ⓐ : 25   : 17   : 8

Ⓑ : 30   : 15   : 5

⑨   The spinner is spun 50 times.

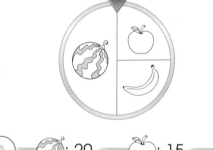

Ⓐ : 20   : 15   : 15

Ⓑ : 25   : 12   : 13

⑩   A ball is picked 50 times.

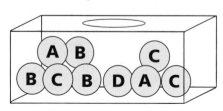

Ⓐ   **A:** 10   **B:** 15   **C:** 15   **D:** 10

Ⓑ   **A:** 11   **B:** 17   **C:** 17   **D:** 5

Read what the boy says and complete the table. Then answer the questions.

⑪

Sum of Two Dice

+	1	2	3	4	5	6
1						
2						
3						
4						
5						
6						

I will roll two dice and add to find the sum. The sums are the outcomes.

a. List all 11 possible outcomes: _____

b. Put the outcomes in order from the least frequent to the most frequent.

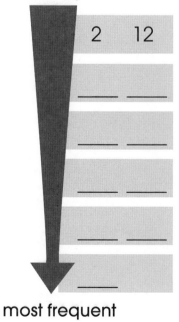

least frequent

2   12

___ ___

___ ___

___ ___

___ ___

___

most frequent

c. Predict the frequency of each outcome if he rolls the two dice 36 times.

- 2: _____   • 3: _____

- 4: _____   • 5: _____

- 6: _____   • 7: _____

- 8: _____   • 9: _____

- 10: _____   • 11: _____

- 12: _____

d. The boy thinks that if he rolls the dice 50 times, he will get an even sum about 25 times. Is he correct? Explain.

_____

_____

LEVEL 3
APPLICATIONS

1 Addition and Subtraction

- adding and subtracting whole numbers in word problems

Try It

984 candies were sold on Day 1 and 745 candies were sold on Day 2. How many candies were sold in all?

[ ] ◯ [ ] = [ ]

[ ] candies were sold in all.

Read This

To solve word problems, always look for keywords to determine what operation to use. Then identify the numbers you need to solve the problem.

Solve the problems. Show your work.

① Ben had 428 marbles. He gave Emily 199 marbles. How many marbles does he have left?

_____ marbles

② Amy has 183 green marbles and 214 blue marbles. How many marbles does she have altogether?

_____ marbles

③ Andrew bought 89 marbles. He adds them to his jar of 280 marbles. How many marbles are there in his jar now?

_____ marbles

④ Joe had 317 marbles and he bought 88 more. Then Jill gave him 95 marbles. How many marbles does Joe have?

_____ marbles

⑤ I have 507 marbles. If I give 197 away, how many marbles will I have left?

_____ marbles

A singer performed in four cities. The table shows the number of people who attended the performance in each city. Use the table to answer the questions.

⑥

City	Toronto	Montreal	Calgary	Vancouver
Attendance	3590	2945	1782	2595

a. How many people in total attended his concerts in Toronto and Montreal?

_____

_____ people

b. How many people in total attended his concerts in Calgary and Vancouver?

_____

_____ people

c. How many more people attended the concert in Vancouver than the concert in Calgary?

_____

_____ people

d. 1827 children attended the concert in Montreal. How many adults attended the concert?

_____

_____ adults

e. The singer expects to have 260 more people attend his concert in Toronto next year. How many people are expected?

_____

_____ people

f. The singer expects to have 290 fewer people attend his concert in Calgary next year. How many people are expected?

_____

_____ people

LEVEL 3 – APPLICATIONS

The table shows the distance Emily travelled on her bike last week. Use the table to solve the problems. Show your work.

⑦

Day	Mon	Tue	Wed	Thu	Fri	Sat	Sun
Distance (m)	876	1328	829	1515	1372	686	1425

a. How far did Emily bike altogether on Monday and Tuesday?

_____

b. How far did Emily bike altogether on the weekend?

_____

c. How much farther did Emily bike on Thursday than on Saturday?

_____

d. How much farther did Emily bike on Friday than on Monday?

_____

e. If Emily wants to bike 1100 m on Monday, how much farther will she have to bike compared to last Monday?

_____

f.

How far did I bike altogether...

• on Wednesday, Thursday, and Friday?

_____

• last week?

_____

Solve the problems. Show your work.

⑧ A soccer stadium has 970 seats in Section 1, 1125 seats in Section 2, and 2540 seats in Section 3.

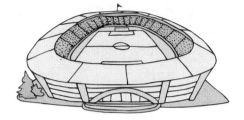

  a. How many seats are there in Sections 2 and 3 altogether?

  _____

  b. How many more seats are there in Section 3 than Section 1?

  _____

⑨ Cameron helps out in the school library. The library has 3411 storybooks, 2936 picture books, and 424 French books.

  a. How many storybooks and picture books are there in the library?

  _____

  b. How many more storybooks are there than French books?

  _____

⑩ In Greenville, 2579 families have dogs, 692 families have cats with patterned fur, and 299 families have black cats.

  a. How many families have cats?

  _____

  b. How many more families have dogs than cats?

  _____

2 Multiplication and Division

• solving multiplication and division problems involving 2-digit numbers

Try It

Each box holds 30 books. If there are 6 boxes, how many books are there in all?

There are ☐ books in all.

Read This

In general, multiplication questions ask you to find the total. Division questions ask how many are in each group or how many equal groups there are.

Check the correct number sentence and solve each problem. Show your work.

① 24 scouts are lined up in 3 rows. How many scouts are there in each row?

(A) 24 x 3 = _____

(B) 24 ÷ 3 = _____

There are _____ scouts in each row.

② A teacher has 16 boxes of crayons. Each box has 4 crayons. How many crayons does the teacher have?

(A) 16 x 4 = _____

(B) 16 ÷ 4 = _____

The teacher has _____ crayons.

③ Will and Helen share a bag of 18 candies equally. How many candies does each child get?

(A) 18 x 2 = _____

(B) 18 ÷ 2 = _____

Each child gets _____ candies.

Solve the problems. Show your work.

④ 84 apples are packed into bags of 7. How many bags of apples are there?

_____ = _____

There are _____ bags of apples.

⑤ A ribbon is 96 cm long. If Sally cuts it into 4 equal strips, how long will each strip be?

_____ = _____

Each strip will be _____ cm long.

⑥ Mom bought 2 bags of straws with 48 straws in each bag. How many straws did Mom buy?

_____ = _____

Mom bought _____ straws.

⑦ Ryan earns $32 weekly. How much does he earn in 3 weeks?

_____ = _____

He earns $_____ in 3 weeks.

⑧ 36 players are split into 3 teams. How many players are there on each team?

_____ = _____

There are _____ players on each team.

⑨ A farmer planted 5000 stalks of corn in rows of 100. How many rows of corn did he plant?

Tips Remember, you can multiply or divide a number by 10, 100, or 1000 by adding or removing the correct number of zeros.

e.g.

$52 \times 1\underline{00} = 52\underline{00}$
↑
added 2 zeros

$4000 \div 1\underline{0} = 400$
↑
removed 1 zero

He planted _____ rows of corn.

⑩ 10 cities will compete in a baseball tournament. If each city sends a team of 12 players, how many players will play in the tournament?

_____ players will play in the tournament.

⑪ There are 2500 residents in an apartment building. If each floor has 100 residents, how many floors does the building have?

The building has _____ floors.

⑫ 1000 families participate in a recycling program. If each family recycles 20 cans every week, how many cans will the families recycle weekly altogether?

They will recycle _____ cans weekly altogether.

⑬ There are 1500 windows on a skyscraper. If each floor has 100 windows, how many floors does the skyscraper have?

The skyscraper has _____ floors.

⑭ Samantha has put 97 sandwiches equally into 7 bags and has some left over.

   a. How many sandwiches are there in each bag?

Tips

Some division questions ask for the remainders only. Read the questions carefully.

_____

   b. How many sandwiches are left over?

_____

⑮ A class of 29 students is divided into 3 equal groups.

   a. How many students are there in each group?

_____

   b. How many students are not in a group?

_____

⑯ 8 friends share a tub of gumballs. Each friend gets a dozen gumballs. 2 gumballs are left. How many gumballs were there in the tub to start with?

GUMBALLS

_____

Mixed Operations with Whole Numbers

- solving word problems involving addition, subtraction, multiplication, and division

Try It

There are 878 students at Summit Public School. If 369 students wear glasses, how many students do not?

☐ ◯ ☐ = ☐

☐ students do not wear glasses.

Follow the steps below to solve word problems.

❶ Identify the keywords.
❷ Circle important numbers.
❸ Draw a picture if needed.
❹ Decide what operation to use.
❺ Solve the problem.
❻ Write a concluding sentence.

Solve the problems. Show your work.

① Alan has 5 bags of 26 marbles each.

a. How many marbles does he have in all?

_____ = _____

He has _____ marbles in all.

b. Jill has 870 more marbles than Alan. How many marbles does she have?

_____ = _____

She has _____ marbles.

c. Jill puts her marbles equally into 100 bags. How many marbles are in each bag?

_____ = _____

_____ marbles are in each bag.

d. Ken has 269 fewer marbles than Jill. How many marbles does Ken have?

_____ = _____

Ken has _____ marbles.

Mrs. Willy runs a bakery. Help her solve the problems.

② Mrs. Willy made a two-tier cake.

  a. What is the difference in weight between the 2 tiers?

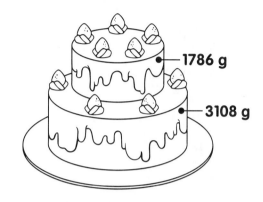

1786 g

3108 g

  The difference is _____ g.

  b. What is the total weight?

  The total weight is _____ g.

③ Mrs. Willy's macarons come in 8 flavours. Last week, she made 18 macarons in each flavour. How many macarons did she make in all?

  She made _____ macarons in all.

④ 6 fruit cakes were sold for $144. How much was each fruit cake?

  Each fruit cake was $_____ .

⑤
  I have 4 trays of 12 cupcakes. I want to pack all the cupcakes into boxes of 6.

  How many boxes does Mrs. Willy need?

  She needs _____ boxes.

Read about the players' scores in the two online games. Find the answers to complete the table. Then answer the questions.

⑥

| A | This score was 2019 points higher than the one Erica got in Space Bonkers. | 1 2 3 6 ◯ 2 0 1 9 |

| B | Tom got 87 points in each of the 9 rounds of Space Bonkers. |

| C | This score is 182 points lower than James's in the same game. |

| D | The boys got a total score of 3229 in Castle Quest. |

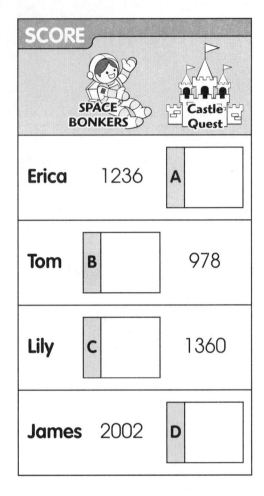

⑦ What is the total score that the girls got in

   a. Space Bonkers?

   b. Castle Quest?

_____   _____

⑧ One of the players said, "I got 136 points in each of the 10 rounds of this game." Which player was it? Which game did he or she play?

_____

Solve the problems. Show your work.

⑨ Stanley divides 74 eggs equally into 4 cartons. How many eggs are there in each carton? How many eggs are left?

_____

⑩ A box contains 36 cookies. If Heather buys 7 boxes of cookies, how many cookies will she have in all?

_____

⑪ Leonard Farm had 9272 saplings. After 5593 saplings were delivered to a local community, how many were left on the farm?

_____

⑫ Charles has 20 stickers in his collection. He arranges his stickers into rows of 9. How many stickers are there in the final row?

_____

⑬ A bag has 38 dog treats. If Ron puts 7 treats into each dog bowl, how many dog bowls can he fill? How many treats will be left?

_____

⑭ I picked 763 cherries on Day 1 and 872 cherries on Day 2.

How many cherries were picked in all?

_____

4 Fractions

• solving word problems involving fractions

A pie was cut into 8 equal pieces. Amy ate 2 pieces. Colour to show how much of the pie Amy ate. Write the fraction.

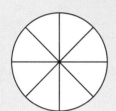

Amy ate ⬚ of the pie.

When solving word problems involving fractions, you can draw pictures using simple shapes like squares, circles, and rectangles to help visualize the problems.

Colour the diagram. Then answer the questions.

① Aunt Jenny baked a brownie. She cut it into 10 equal pieces.

a. Colour to show how much of the brownie was eaten by each child.

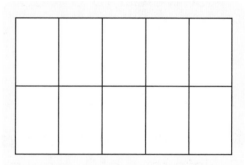

- red: Ben ate 2 pieces.

- green: Jen ate 1 piece.

- yellow: Tim ate 3 pieces.

b. What fraction of the brownie did each child eat?

- Ben: _____   • Jen: _____   • Tim: _____

c. What fraction of the brownie was eaten?

_____

d. What fraction of the brownie is left?

_____

e. Which two children ate $\frac{5}{10}$ of the brownie in all?

_____

Find the answers using the diagrams.

② Jon finished $\frac{1}{4}$ of his assignment on Monday and $\frac{3}{8}$ on Tuesday. On which day did he finish more of his assignment?

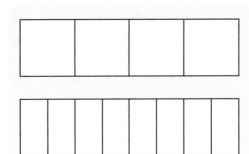

_____

③ Amelia baked an apple pie and a cherry pie. $\frac{2}{3}$ of the apple pie and $\frac{5}{9}$ of the cherry pie were eaten. Which pie had more of it eaten?

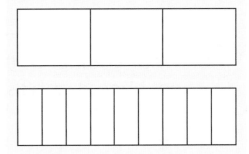

_____

④ Caleb is building a log cabin in his backyard. He finished $\frac{3}{10}$ of it on Monday, $\frac{1}{2}$ on Tuesday, and $\frac{1}{5}$ on Wednesday.

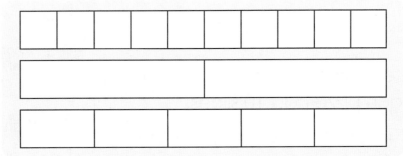

a. On which day did Caleb get the most work done on the cabin?

_____

b. On which day did Caleb get the least work done on the cabin?

_____

c. Did Caleb finish the cabin after the 3 days?

_____

Answer the questions.

⑤ Angeline surveyed her classmates about their favourite fruits. She recorded the results in the chart.

a. What fraction of Angeline's classmates

- chose apples?

  _____

- chose oranges?

  _____

b. What fraction of the class did not choose apples?

  _____

c. If the child who chose bananas changed to apples instead, what fraction of Angeline's classmates chose apples?

  _____

Favourite Fruits	
Fruit	No. of Classmates
apples	3
oranges	2
bananas	1
grapes	3
peaches	1

Tips

To write the fractions, you have to find the total number of classmates surveyed first (the denominator). Then find the number for each choice (the numerator).

← numerator; the parts being considered

← denominator; the total number of parts

⑥ Mrs. Winter ordered two pizzas for a party. Each pizza had 10 slices.

a. What fraction of each pizza was eaten?

 : _____

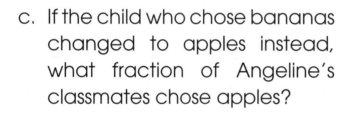 : _____

b. What fraction of the children ate

- 2 slices of  ?   _____

- 1 slice of ?   _____

Hawaiian Pizza

1 slice: Elly, Gabe, Jude
2 slices: Eva, Ivan, Ron

Pepperoni Pizza

1 slice: Elly, Jude
2 slices: Sally, Michael

Answer the questions. Use the space to draw diagrams if needed.

⑦ Judy and Elsa shared a cheesecake. Judy ate $\frac{1}{5}$ and Elsa ate $\frac{2}{5}$. Who had more cheesecake?

_____

⑧ Connie ran $\frac{3}{4}$ of a trail yesterday and $\frac{2}{3}$ today. Did she run more yesterday or today?

_____

⑨ Ronald ate $\frac{1}{5}$ of a pie and Meghan ate $\frac{3}{10}$. Who ate more pie?

_____

⑩ Three children measured their heights. Ashley was $\frac{9}{10}$ m, Lia was $\frac{7}{8}$ m, and Cally was $\frac{6}{9}$ m. Who was the tallest?

_____

⑪ Zack reads $\frac{1}{10}$ of his new book each day. How much of the book will he have read after a week?

_____

⑫ Jared's water bottle is $\frac{1}{2}$ full. Joe's water bottle is $\frac{3}{5}$ empty. Whose water bottle has more water?

_____

5 Decimals

- solving word problems with decimals

Two ropes measure 2.1 m and 1.6 m.
What is the difference in length?

The difference is ☐ m.

Read This

Remember to align the decimal points when adding or subtracting decimals. If needed, add zeros to the numbers to keep them in place.

e.g. 5 − 4.2 = ?

5 − 4.2 = ☐ 0.8

$$\begin{array}{r} 5.0 \\ -\ 4.2 \\ \hline 0.8 \end{array}$$
↑
align

Read the table and answer the questions.

① Jason recorded the heights of his friends in the table.

Heights of Jason's Friends				
Name	Judy	Emily	Nicky	Keith
Height	1.3 m	1.1 m	1.2 m	1.4 m

a. Who is the tallest?

b. Who is shorter than Keith but taller than Nicky?

_____   _____

c. How much taller is Judy than Nicky?

_____

d. What is the difference in height between the tallest child and the shortest one?

_____

Use the map to solve the problems. Show your work.

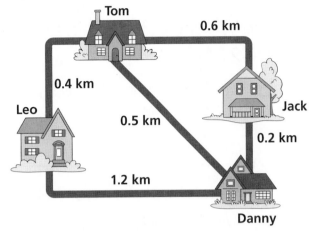

② Tom left his house to drop off a book at Jack's house. Then he went to visit Danny. How far did he walk?

_____

③ If Tom did not have to drop off the book at Jack's but went straight to Danny's instead, how much less would he walk?

_____

④ Does Leo live closer to Tom or Danny? How much closer?

_____

⑤ Jack went to Leo's house. How far did he walk if he passed by

  a. Tom's house?   b. Danny's house?

_____   _____

⑥

I met up with Danny first and then went to Leo's house to play basketball. I travelled a total of 1.7 km.

Is this boy Jack or Tom?

_____

Janice swims regularly. Solve the problems. Show your work.

⑦ On Wednesday, Janice swam for 1.3 h. On Thursday, she swam for 2.5 h.

   a. How many hours did she swim in all?

   _____

   b. How much longer did Janice swim for on Thursday than Wednesday?

   _____

⑧ Janice swam some laps and timed herself. Her times for the first 3 laps were 1.5 min, 1.4 min, and 1.6 min.

   a. How long did it take Janice to complete the 3 laps?

   _____

   b. It took Janice 1 min and 30 s to complete the fourth lap. How many minutes in total did it take Janice to complete all 4 laps?

   _____

⑨

> Yesterday, I swam the first lap in 1.5 min and the next two laps in 1.7 min each.

How long did it take her to swim the 3 laps?

_____

Solve the problems. Show your work.

⑩ Abe finished a sprint in 18 s and Rich finished it in 16.3 s. Who was faster? By how much?

_____

⑪ A honeydew weighs 2.4 kg. A watermelon weighs 1.7 kg more. What is the weight of the watermelon?

_____

⑫ A roll of red ribbon is 2.5 m long and a roll of blue ribbon is 0.6 m shorter. What is the total length of 2 rolls of blue ribbon?

_____

⑬ Tree A is 4.2 m tall. Tree B is 0.7 m taller than Tree A and 0.5 m shorter than Tree C. How tall is Tree C?

_____

⑭ It was 6.7°C in the morning. The temperature rose by 3.3°C in the afternoon and then dropped by 2.5°C in the evening. What was the temperature in the evening?

_____

⑮ Ariel had $45.20 in her piggy bank and got $4.90 from her parents for doing chores. Does she have enough money to buy the headphones shown?

$49.50

_____

6 Money

- solving word problems involving money

Lucy has $15. If she spends $11.35 on lunch, how much will she have left?

She will have $ ⬚ left.

Remember that $1 equals 100¢.

e.g. 20 cents = $0.20

   1 dollar 5 cents = $1.05

___

Do conversions when needed to solve problems.

Answer the questions.

① Joe has 2 coins in his pocket. Their total value is $0.30.

  a. Which coins does he have?

    _____

  b. If he buys a candy for 20¢, how much will he have left?

    _____

②
> I paid $3.15 for a sandwich using the fewest coins.

Which coins did she use?

_____

③
> I have $5.50 in coins left. 12 of the coins are quarters and the rest are dimes.

How many dimes does she have?

_____

Solve the problems.   Show your work.

④   Jason had $16.25 in his piggy bank. His mom gave him $5.80 more. How much does he have now?

_____

⑤   Anna bought 2 cupcakes for $1.60 each.

a. What was the total cost?

_____

b. If she paid for them with a $5 bill, what was her change?

_____

⑥   James has $50.20 and his brother Zack has $36.75.

a. How much more does James have than Zack?

_____

b. The boys want to buy a gift for their mom. Can they afford a purse that costs $87?

_____

Read the menu. Solve the problems. Show your work.

⑦ How much does it cost for

a. 1 hamburger and 1 can of pop?

_____

b. 1 pizza and 1 carton of milk?

_____

Sam's Stand

hamburger	$4.49
pizza	$11.90
hot dog	$2.35
fries	$1.75
pop	$2.50
milk	$2.15

⑧ I'll buy 1 hot dog and 1 carton of milk. How much do I need?

_____

⑨ I paid for a pizza with a $20 bill. What was my change?

_____

⑩ I have 2 toonies. How much more do I need for a hamburger?

_____

⑪ I paid for a pizza with three $5 bills. What was my change?

_____

Rainbow Store's cash register has broken down. Help the cashier solve the problems. Then draw the fewest bills and coins to show the change.

⑫

a. Joan paid for a hat and a pack of hair clips with a $20 bill. What was her change?

Joan's Change

_____

b. Alan paid for a scarf and a hat with a $50 bill. What was his change?

Alan's Change

_____

c. Katie paid for a balloon and a pair of sunglasses with five $5 bills. What was her change?

Katie's Change

_____

LEVEL 3 – APPLICATIONS

7 Perimeter and Area

- solving word problems involving the perimeter and area

Try It

Gilbert wants to find out how many tiles he needs to cover the floor of his living room. Does he need to find the perimeter or the area of the floor?

He needs to find the _____ .

Read This

Perimeter: the total distance around a shape

Area: the space a shape covers

↑
the perimeter of the square

↑
the area of the square

Check whether the perimeter or area needs to be considered for each scenario.

① How much wood do I need to frame this drawing?

○ perimeter   ○ area

② How many planks of wood do I need to build the deck?

○ perimeter   ○ area

③ How much fencing do I need for my backyard?

○ perimeter   ○ area

④ How many stickers do I need to cover the page?

○ perimeter   ○ area

⑤ How much grass seed do I need to cover the lawn?

○ perimeter   ○ area

Draw all possible rectangles with the given perimeter and area. Label them and complete the tables. Then put a check mark for each correct statement.

⑥

Perimeter:
12 centimetres

Perimeter (centimetres)	Area (square centimetres)
A	
B	
C	

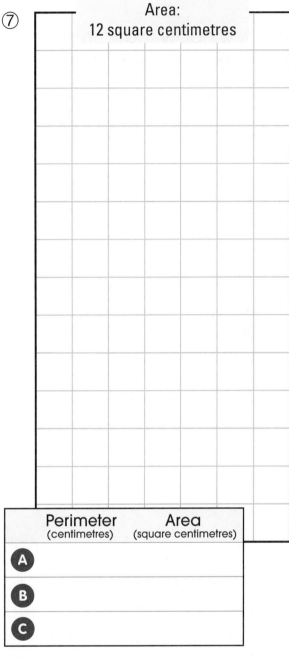

⑦

Area:
12 square centimetres

Perimeter (centimetres)	Area (square centimetres)
A	
B	
C	

A Rectangles that have the same perimeter must also have the same area.

B A rectangle that has a smaller area does not necessarily have a smaller perimeter.

A A rectangle that has a greater perimeter also has a greater area.

B Rectangles with the same area can have different perimeters.

Read each question. Check to show whether it involves the perimeter or area. Sketch the shape and label it with the given measurements. Then solve the problem.

⑧ A window measures 16 dm in width and 9 dm in height. How big is the window?

○ **perimeter**   ○ area

Tips

Draw on the sketched shape to indicate the parts required to solve the problem.

_____

⑨ Laura's lawn measures 16 m by 9 m. How much fencing is needed to enclose the lawn?

○ **perimeter**   ○ area

_____

⑩ A rug measures 4 m by 2 m. How much of the floor does the rug cover?

○ **perimeter**   ○ area

_____

⑪ Jean wants to add frills around a mat that is 3 m by 3 m. How much frill material is needed?

○ **perimeter**   ○ area

_____

⑫ Alan wants to cut wooden strips to frame a picture that is 15 cm by 20 cm. How much wood does he need?

○ **perimeter**   ○ area

_____

Solve the problems. Show your work.

⑬ Mr. Jenkins has a 2-m-long wooden strip. Is the wooden strip long enough to frame a rectangular poster that is 20 cm by 30 cm? If so, will any wooden strip be left over? How much?

_____

⑭ The side of a square bulletin board is 50 cm long. How big is the bulletin board?

_____

⑮ A square quilt has a side length of 20 dm. A rectangular quilt measures 8 dm by 100 cm.

   a. Which quilt is larger?

Tips

Do conversions to make all measurements the same measuring unit.

_____

   b. If frills are added around each quilt, which quilt needs more frills? By how much?

_____

⑯

> I purchased a bundle of wooden planks to build a patio in my backyard. Each plank measures 100 cm by 10 cm.

If his patio is 2 m by 6 m, how many wooden planks does he need?

_____

8 Mass, Capacity, and Volume

- solving word problems involving the mass, capacity, and volume

Try It

Fill in the blanks with the most appropriate measuring units.

Read This

Below are the measuring units for mass, capacity, and volume.

- Mass: mg, g, kg
- Capacity: mL, L
- Volume: cubic centimetres (cm³)

- Elsa weighs 50 _____ .

- The jug can hold 2 _____ of juice.

- This feather is 64 _____ lighter than the paper clip.

- I drank 150 _____ of water.

Look at the food items and their masses. Answer the questions.

① How much heavier are the sausages than the cornflakes? _____

② Which food item is 200 g lighter than the bananas? _____

③ Which food item has a mass closest to 1 kg? _____

④ Which food item has a mass closest to 100 g? _____

⑤ Which food item is 10 times as heavy as the salt? _____

⑥ What is the mass of 1 banana? _____

⑦ List the food items in order from heaviest to lightest.

_____

Potatoes 10 kg

Cornflakes 550 g

Sausages 950 g

55 g Salt

750 g

Look at the containers and their capacities. Fill in the blanks and answer the question.

250 mL   Milk 1 L   Soap 750 mL   Syrup 500 mL   3 L

⑧ _____ mugs of water can fill up 1 milk carton.

⑨ _____ bottles of syrup can fill up 1 milk carton.

⑩ _____ mugs of water can fill up 1 soap bottle.

⑪ _____ cartons of milk can fill up 1 bucket.

⑫ _____ bottles of syrup can fill up 1 bucket.

⑬ _____ bottles of soap can fill up 1 bucket.

⑭ List the containers in order from smallest capacity to greatest.

_____

Answer the questions about the structures below.

⑮

I built structures with my centimetre cubes.

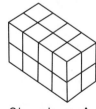 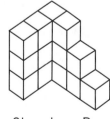 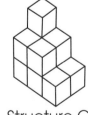

Structure A   Structure B   Structure C

a. Which structure has the greatest volume? _____

b. Which structure has the smallest volume? _____

c. If Structure C is rebuilt into a rectangular prism, what will its dimensions be? _____

For each problem, write whether it involves the mass, capacity, or volume in the box. Then solve the problem. Show your work.

⑯ Ms. Lee has 3 water bottles.

    a. If each bottle can hold 500 mL of water, how much water can the 3 bottles hold in all?

    ☐ _____

    b. If each bottle weighs 350 g, how much do the 3 bottles weigh altogether?

    ☐ _____

⑰ Carla built towers with centimetre cubes.

    a. Her first tower measures 3 cm in length, 1 cm in width, and 6 cm in height. Check the tower Carla built. How much space does it take up?

    ☐ _____

    b. Carla built another tower with the same number of blocks as the first one. Each tower weighs 250 g. How much do the 2 towers weigh in total?

    ☐ _____

⑱ Jack built a cube that has a side length of 2 cm. Draw the cube on the grid. How much space does the cube take up?

    ☐ _____

Solve the problems.

⑲ Each bag of flour weighs 200 g. How many bags does Irene need to buy if she wants 1 kg of flour?

Mass:
1 g = 1000 mg
1 kg = 1000 g

Capacity:
1 L = 1000 mL

_____

⑳ Betsy needs 4 L of milk for baking. If each carton has 500 mL of milk, how many cartons does she need?

_____

㉑ Each teaspoon holds 5 g of sugar. If Alan added 2 teaspoons of sugar to his tea, how many milligrams of sugar did he add?

_____

㉒ Wanda has 4 bowls. Each bowl weighs 200 g and can hold 8 L of fruit punch.

　a. What is the total mass of the bowls?

_____

　b. How much fruit punch can the 4 bowls hold in all?

_____

㉓ Eric built 2 towers with centimetre cubes. He used 50 cubes for the big tower and 18 cubes for the small one. How much more space does the big tower take up than the small one?

_____

9 Shapes and Solids

- solving word problems involving shapes and solids

Try It

Marco cut out 5 squares, 3 triangles, and 2 rectangles from construction paper. How many quadrilaterals did he cut out?

He cut out _____ quadrilaterals.

Read This

Properties of Shapes:
- number of sides*
- number of angles
- length of the sides
- number of lines of symmetry
- parallel sides

e.g. ← isosceles triangle

- 3 sides; 2 of the sides are equal
- 3 angles
- 1 line of symmetry

*All polygons with 4 sides are called quadrilaterals.

Benson made a drawing using shapes as shown. Answer the questions about the drawing. Then colour.

① How many quadrilaterals are there in the drawing?

_____

② Which quadrilaterals in the drawing

a. have parallel sides?

_____

_____

b. have right angles?

_____

_____

c. have 4 lines of symmetry?

_____

_____

③ Do the colouring.

 red

not quadrilaterals

 blue

quadrilaterals with lines of symmetry

green

quadrilaterals without right angles

The children cut out some shapes from construction paper. Answer the questions about their shapes.

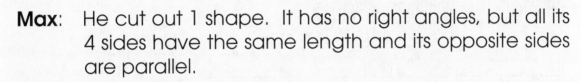

④ **Lea**: She cut out 4 triangles, 9 circles, and 7 squares.

Kyle: He cut out 9 pentagons, 3 rhombuses, and 1 trapezoid.

Max: He cut out 1 shape. It has no right angles, but all its 4 sides have the same length and its opposite sides are parallel.

Ali: She cut out 1 shape. It has no right angles, but it has 2 pairs of parallel sides and 2 pairs of equal sides.

a. How many quadrilaterals did Lea cut out? _____

b. How many of Kyle's shapes have parallel sides? _____

c. Sketch Max's and Ali's shapes and write the names of the shapes.

Max	Ali
_____	_____

d. One child said, "I drew a shape that has 2 right angles and no lines of symmetry." Who said this? Sketch the shape and name it.

_____

e. If Max cut the shape he drew in half, what shapes could he get?

_____

Answer the questions.

⑤

My solid has 2 bases. It is a _____ .
$\quad$ pyramid/prism

⑥ Joey's solid has 1 base. The base is in the shape of a square. Is it a pyramid or prism? Sketch the solid and name it.

_____

⑦ Dennis's solid has 6 faces, 8 vertices, and 12 edges that are the same length.

a. What is the solid? Sketch it.

_____

b. Evelyn's solid is similar to Dennis's but has 4 rectangular faces. What is the solid? Sketch it.

_____

⑧ William's solid has 12 edges that are not the same length.

a. What 2 solids could it be? Sketch one of them.

_____

b. If William's solid has 7 vertices and 7 faces, what is the solid? Sketch it.

_____

Answer the questions about solids.

⑨ Read the descriptions. Sketch the nets and the solids they form. Then name the solids.

a. Dorothy's net has 1 hexagon and 6 triangles.

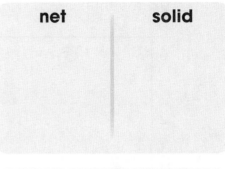

_____

b. Michael's net has 2 pentagons and 5 rectangles.

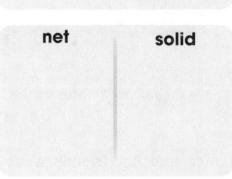

_____

⑩ Oscar has 2 nets. Net A has 6 identical squares and Net B has 6 identical rectangles. Which one can be folded into a solid? Name the solid.

_____

⑪ Jessica has 6 balls of clay and a pack of toothpicks. What solids can she make if she uses up all 6 balls of clay?

_____

⑫ Keith has a skeleton of a triangular prism. Each side of the base of the prism is equal in length. If he takes the prism apart and uses the materials to build a hexagonal pyramid, how many more balls of clay and sticks does he need?

_____

10 Grid Maps

- solving word problems involving grid maps

Try It

Leo is looking for the mountains on a map. What are the coordinates of the mountains?

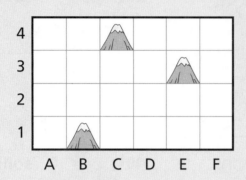

When locating things on a grid map with coordinates, locate the letters first (which run horizontally), and then locate the numbers (which run vertically).

♥ is at <u>D2</u>.

The coordinates of the mountains are _____ .

Janice and her friends went camping at Camp Kiwi. See the grid map and answer the questions.

①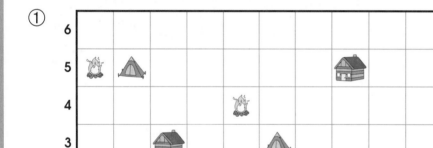

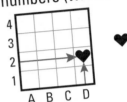

Legend

 tent

 cabin

 campfire spot

Find the coordinates of the...

a. tents: _____

b. cabins: _____

c. campfire spots: _____

A forest covers the areas at D5, E5, and F5. Colour the forest green on the map.

② Janice and her friends stayed at the cabin at C3.

a. Where is the closest campfire spot?

_____

b. How should they go to get to the campfire spot?

_____

③ Janice made a new friend at the campsite. Her new friend was staying at the tent farthest away from Janice's cabin.

a. Where is her friend's tent?

_____

b. How should her friend go from her tent to Janice's cabin?

_____

Complete the grid map. Then answer the questions.

④ Construction workers are placing pylons on a construction site at A3, C6, D1, and F4. Draw △ to show where the pylons are.

⑤ The ⛏ shows where the workers need to dig to fix some pipes. What are the coordinates of these locations?

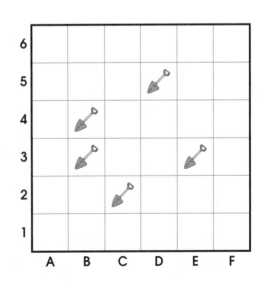

_____

_____

⑥ An underground electric cable runs from B1 to B6. At which locations do the workers need to be careful when digging?

_____

Use the grid map to answer the questions about the park.

⑦

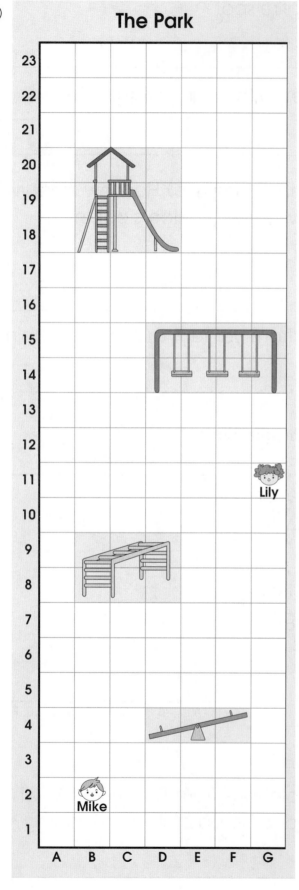

The Park

a. What are the coordinates of
   - the swings?

   _____

   _____

   - the monkey bars?

   _____

   _____

   - the see-saw?

   _____

   _____

   - the slide?

   _____

   _____

b. Mike went 4 squares to the right and 12 squares up. Which playground equipment did he go to?

   _____

c. Lily went 5 squares to the left and 3 squares down. Which playground equipment did she go to?

   _____

Answer the questions to help Pirate Pete navigate Rocky River and get to the treasure.

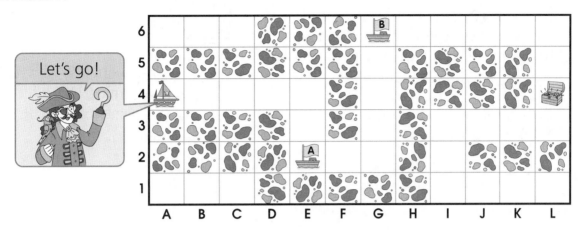

⑧ What are the coordinates of Stations A and B and the treasure?

_____

⑨ How should Pirate Pete sail to get from

a. the start to Station A?

_____

b. Station A to Station B?

_____

c. Station B to the treasure?

_____

The coordinates of the children's seats in a classroom are shown. Answer the questions.

⑩ Who sits beside Liza?

_____

⑪ Who sits in the same row as Anne?

_____

Ken: C2	Jane: D7
Liza: A5	Joe: E1
Anne: B7	Leo: B5
Sue: C3	Fred: E2

11 Patterning

- solving word problems involving patterning

Tracy saves 2 coins each day. If she has 6 coins on Day 1, how many coins will she have by Day 4? Complete the table.

Read This

When solving word problems involving patterning, look for the starting number and the pattern rule.

Day	1	2	3	4
Number of Coins	6	8		

She will have _____ coins by Day 4.

Complete the table for each problem and answer the questions.

① Gabe bought 5 marbles in Week 1. Each week after that he bought 2 more marbles than the week before.

a. Complete the table.

Week	1	2	3	4	5	6	7	8
Number of Marbles	5							

b. How many marbles did he buy in Week 5?

_____

c. In which week did he buy 17 marbles?

_____

d. How many marbles did he buy in all in the first 6 weeks?

_____

e. How many marbles will he buy in Week 10?

_____

② I'm building a tower with blocks. Each layer has 1 block fewer than the layer below it. The first layer has 10 blocks.

Lily

a. Complete the table.

Layer	1	2	3	4	5
Number of Blocks	10				

b. How many blocks are there in Layer 4?

_____

c. If Lily has 27 blocks in her tower, how many layers are there?

_____

d. How many blocks are there in total in 5 layers?

_____

③ Joe ran a 6-lap race. He finished the first lap in 15 s. After that, each lap took him 5 s longer than the previous lap.

a. Complete the table.

Lap	1	2	3	4	5	6
Time for Each Lap (s)	15					

b. Which lap took him 30 s to finish?

_____

c. How long did it take Joe to finish the final lap?

_____

d. How long did it take Joe to complete the race?

_____

Use tables to solve the patterning problems.

④ Mrs. Grey has 100 crayons. Each week, she gives out 10 crayons.

a. Complete the table to show the total number of crayons she has given out from Week 1 to Week 6.

Week	
Total Number of Crayons Given Out	

b. How many crayons have been given out in total by Week 4?

_____

c. How many crayons does she have left by the end of Week 6?

_____

d. In which week will the last batch of crayons be given out?

_____

⑤ On the first day of January, Samuel had a jar of 128 candies. He and his friends ate half of the candies each month.

a. Complete the table to show how many candies were in the jar each month from January to June.

Month	
Number of Candies in Jar	

b. In which month were there 8 candies left?

_____

c. How many candies in total were eaten by the end of March?

_____

⑥ Judy has 5¢ in her piggy bank in the 1st week, 10¢ in the 2nd week, and 15¢ in the 3rd week. If the pattern continues, how much will she have by the 7th week?

_____

⑦ Liam has 7 stickers in his sticker book. He starts adding 4 stickers to his book each day. How many stickers will he have after 8 days?

_____

⑧ Catherine completes 3 worksheets on Monday, 5 on Tuesday, and 7 on Wednesday. If the pattern continues,

   a. how many worksheets will she complete on Friday?

   _____

   b. on which day will she complete 13 worksheets?

   _____

⑨

   I bake 7 pies and 12 cakes on Monday, 10 pies and 10 cakes on Tuesday, and 13 pies and 8 cakes on Wednesday.

   a. How many pies will she bake on Friday?

   _____

   b. How many cakes will she bake on Sunday?

   _____

12 Equations

- solving word problems using equations

Try It

Emily had 12 marbles. After giving some to Gabe, she had 8 marbles left. How many marbles did she give away? Check the equation that describes the problem. Use the drawing to help.

Read This

An equation expresses a word problem numerically. To help solve it, draw to visualize the problem and find the answer.

(A) 12 – ? = 8

(B) 12 + ? = 8

○ ○ ○ ○
○ ○ ○ ○
○ ○ ○ ○

She gave away _____ marbles.

Emily and Gabe both have marble collections. Check the equation that describes each problem. Use the drawing to help find the answer.

① Gabe had 15 marbles. Emily hid some of his marbles, leaving him with 9. How many marbles did Emily hide?

(A) 15 – ? = 9   (B) ? – 15 = 9

_____

② Emily had 20 marbles. Then some of them rolled away. She now has 11 marbles. How many marbles rolled away?

(A) 20 + ? = 11   (B) 20 – ? = 11

_____

③ Gabe gave 9 red marbles to Emily. She now has 17 red marbles. How many red marbles did she have to start with?

(A) 9 + ? = 17   (B) 17 + ? = 9

_____

Check the equation that expresses each problem. Then solve it using any method you choose.

④ Alex ate 6 peanuts and has 8 left. How many peanuts did he start with?

Ⓐ $6 + ? = 8$ Ⓑ $? - 6 = 8$

Do your work here.

_____

⑤ Toby gave 12 cards to David. David now has 21 cards. How many cards did David have to start with?

Ⓐ $? + 12 = 21$ Ⓑ $? + 21 = 12$

_____

⑥ Cookies come in boxes of 6. Elliot bought 36 cookies. How many boxes of cookies did he buy?

Ⓐ $6 + ? = 36$ Ⓑ $6 \times ? = 36$

_____

⑦ Sara baked 30 muffins. If there are 10 muffins in a tray, how many trays of muffins did she bake?

Ⓐ $30 \div ? = 10$ Ⓑ $30 \times ? = 10$

_____

⑧ A bus has a capacity of 64 people. How many rows are there on the bus if 4 people can be seated in each row?

Ⓐ $4 \times ? = 64$ Ⓑ $64 - ? = 4$

_____

Match each equation with the word problem that it expresses. Then solve it.

⑨

$$? - 3 = 15 \qquad\qquad ? \div 3 = 15$$
$$3 + ? = 15 \qquad 15 \div ? = 3 \qquad 15 - ? = 3$$

a. Joseph has 3 pencils. How many more pencils does he need to have 15 pencils?

equation

_____

b. Elaine had 15 lollipops. She gave some away and now has 3 left. How many lollipops did she give away?

equation

_____

c. Mr. Jill had a basket of apples. He used 3 apples to make apple pie and now has 15 left. How many apples were in the basket to start with?

equation

_____

d. Lory wants to divide 15 crayons equally into boxes. If 3 pencils fit in each box, how many boxes does she need?

equation

_____

e. Juliet has a bouquet of roses in 3 different colours. If there are 15 roses in each colour, how many roses are there in the bouquet?

equation

_____

⑩

$$6 \times ? = 30 \qquad ? \div 6 = 5$$
$$? + 6 = 30 \qquad ? - 5 = 6 \qquad 30 \div ? = 6$$

a. Joanna put 30 hats into equal stacks. How many hats are there in each stack if there are 6 stacks?

equation

_____

b. A bag can hold 6 oranges. How many bags are needed to hold 30 oranges?

equation

_____

c. Rahil read 5 chapters of a book. He has 6 chapters left. How many chapters are there in the book?

equation

_____

d. Amy has some blocks. If she uses them all to make 6 towers of the same height, each tower will be 5 blocks tall. How many blocks does she have in all?

equation

_____

e.

If I give Daniel 6 blocks, he will have 30 blocks. How many blocks does he have?

equation

_____

13 Graphs

• making graphs and studying them

Try It

Harry surveyed the students at his school on their favourite drinks and recorded the results.

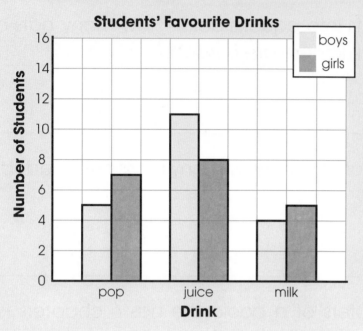

Students' Favourite Drinks

□ boys
■ girls

Read This

A double bar graph compares two sets of data or two aspects of a set of data.

Which drink is the most popular?

_____ is the most popular.

Refer to the graph above to answer the questions.

① Which drink is the least popular?

_____

② How many more boys than girls voted for juice?

_____

③ How many more girls voted for juice than milk?

_____

④ How many students chose juice over pop?

_____

⑤ How many students chose pop over milk?

_____

Lily and Alan did surveys to find out the seasons in which their friends have birthdays. Complete the double bar graph to show the data.

⑥

Number of People		Season			
		Spring	Summer	Fall	Winter
Number of People	by Lily	16	18	12	13
	by Alan	13	16	10	15

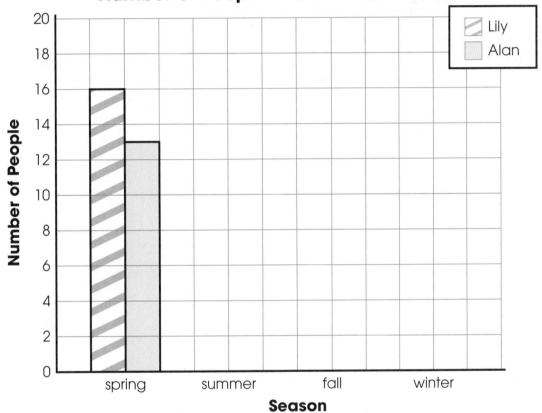

Number of People Born in Each Season

a. Which season has the most birthdays?

_____

b. How many more of Lily's friends were born in summer than fall?

_____

c. How many more of Lily's friends than Alan's were born in fall?

_____

d. Who surveyed more people? By how many?

_____

An arcade's most popular games are Munchball and Spacekins. The scores of a group of 25 players were recorded for each game. Organize the sets of data in the stem-and-leaf plots. Then complete the double bar graph and answer the questions.

⑦

Munchball

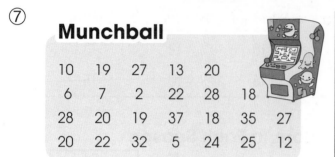

10	19	27	13	20	
6	7	2	22	28	18
28	20	19	37	18	35	27
20	22	32	5	24	25	12

Stem	Leaf

Spacekins

27	19	30	15	12	
29	33	7	25	30	6
31	24	14	25	1	15	39
37	36	35	31	4	10	34

Stem	Leaf

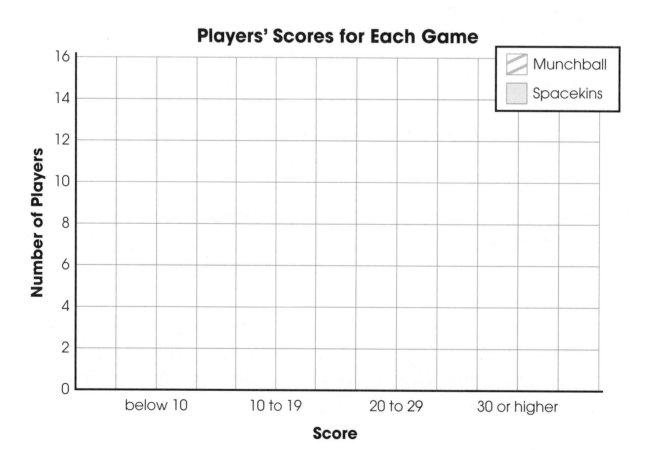

Players' Scores for Each Game

Munchball
Spacekins

Number of Players

16
14
12
10
8
6
4
2
0

below 10   10 to 19   20 to 29   30 or higher

Score

⑧ What are the median and mode scores of

a. Munchball?

_____

b. Spacekins?

_____

⑨ What is the range of the scores for

a. Munchball?

_____

b. Spacekins?

_____

⑩ How many fewer players scored 10 to 19 points than 20 to 29 points in Munchball?

_____

⑪ Janice says, "About half of the players got between 20 and 29 points in this game." Which game is she talking about?

_____

⑫

It seems that players in one of the games often get 30 points or more. If I want to get over 30 points, which game should I play?

_____

14 Probability

- solving word problems involving probability

Try It

A fair coin is flipped. What is the probability of getting heads?

A coin is fair if the probability of either outcome – heads or tails – is the same.

The probability is _____ .

Read This

The more trials we do in an experiment, the closer the result will be to the theoretical frequency.

Draw a tree diagram to show all the possible outcomes of flipping a coin two times. Then do what the boy says and answer the questions.

①

Possible Outcomes of Flipping a Coin 2 Times

Prediction	Result
HH _____ times	
HT	
TH	
TT	

Predict how many times you will get each outcome if you flip the coin twice 20 times. Then flip the coin twice 20 times and record the actual results.

② Compare your predictions with the results. Do you think your predictions will be closer to the results if you repeat the experiment?

_____

_____

Answer the questions about each scenario.

③ Brandon flips a coin.

a. About how many times will he get heads if he flips it 10 times?

_____

b. About how many times will he get tails if he flips it 50 times?

_____

④ There are 3 sets of cards as shown.

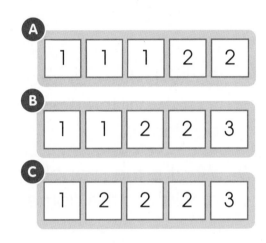

a. William says, "If I pick a card from my set 10 times, I will get about four 1s." Which set is William's? Explain.

_____

_____

b. Oliver says, "If I pick a card from my set 50 times, I will get about thirty 2s." Which set is Oliver's? Explain.

_____

⑤ Kyle has a box of 4 balls as shown.

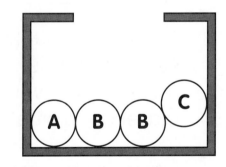

a. If Kyle picks a ball out 20 times, about how many times will he get an "A"?

_____

b. Kyle removes one ball to make the game fair. Which ball does he remove?

_____

Percy created a game using two spinners. Players spin each spinner once. If the spinners land on the same animal, the player wins a prize; otherwise, the player loses.

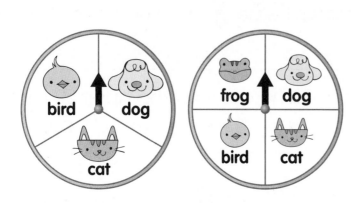

The outcomes on each spinner are equally likely.

⑥ Draw a tree diagram to show all the possible outcomes.

⑦ What is the probability of winning the game?

_____

⑧ What is the probability of losing the game?

_____

⑨ If the game is played 60 times, about how many times will the player get a prize?

_____

⑩ Percy says, "If the game is played 120 times, there will be 70 times where no one wins a prize." Is this reasonable? Explain.

_____

_____

Grade 4
QR Code

QR Code – a quick way to access our fun-filled videos

Our QR code provides you with a quick and easy link to our fun-filled videos, which can help enrich your learning experience while you are working on the workbook. Below is a summary of the topics that the QR code brings you to. You may scan the QR code in each unit to learn about the topic or the QR code on the right to review all the topics you have learned in this book.

Scan this QR code or visit our Download Centre at *www.popularbook.ca*.

The topics introduced with the QR code:

1 **How to Add 4-digit Numbers** (p. 15)
Learn to add 4-digit numbers with regrouping.

2 **How to Subtract 4-digit Numbers** (p. 17)
Learn to subtract 4-digit numbers with regrouping.

3 **Tips and Tricks on Multiplication** (p. 19)
Discover handy tips and tricks for memorizing the times table.

4 **How to Multiply** (p. 23)
Learn to multiply 2-digit numbers by 1-digit numbers with regrouping.

5 **Metric Prefixes** (p. 71)
Investigate the meaning of "kilo", "centi", and "milli".

Level 1

1 Numbers to 10 000

Try It
1326

1. 3213
2. 2450
3. 3206
4. 2099
5. 4405
6. 3278
7. C ; B ; A
8. C ; A ; B
9. 2195 ; 100 ; 90 ; 5 ; ninety-five
10. 4097 ; 4000 + 90 + 7 ;
    four thousand ninety-seven
11. 1480 ; 1000 + 400 + 80 ;
    one thousand four hundred eighty
12. 2809 ; 2000 + 800 + 9 ;
    two thousand eight hundred nine
13. 300
14. 6000
15. 7
16. 5000
17. 80
18. 400
19. 10
20. 2
21. 80
22. 9
23. 300
24. 4000
25a. 1269
b. 1649
26a. 3124
b. 5829
27a. 3024
b. 5160
28a. 4832
b. 6704
29. 1023 ; 3210
30. 8009 ; 9800
31a. 4000

b. 3900

c. 3870

32a. 5000

b. 5000

c. 5020

33a. 7820 ; 7800 ; 8000
b. 6020 ; 6000 ; 6000
c. 8240 ; 8200 ; 8000
d. 2460 ; 2500 ; 2000
e. 8780 ; 8800 ; 9000
f. 3420 ; 3400 ; 3000
g. 1100 ; 1100 ; 1000

2 Addition and Subtraction (1)

Try It

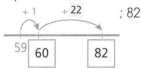
; 82

1. 92

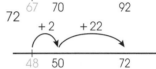

2. 72

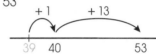

3. 53

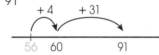

4. 91

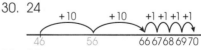

5. 89
6. 86
7. 91
8. 84
9. 79
   2 ; 6
   5 ; 3
   7 ; 9
10. 77
    4 ; 5
    3 ; 2
    7 ; 7
11. 95
    3 ; 7
    5 ; 8
    8 ; 15
    9 ; 5
12. 77
    4 ; 8
    2 ; 9
    6 ; 17
    7 ; 7
13. 44
14. 90
15. 91
16. 51
17. 62
18. 92
19. 70
20. 82
21. 58
22. 33
23. 74
24. 45
25. 95
26. 62
27. 62
28. 77
29. 34
30. 24

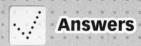

31. 35

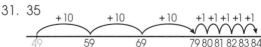

32. 28

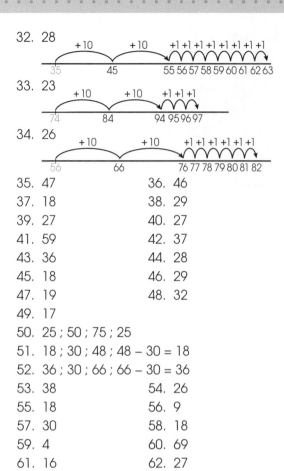

33. 23

34. 26

35. 47   36. 46
37. 18   38. 29
39. 27   40. 27
41. 59   42. 37
43. 36   44. 28
45. 18   46. 29
47. 19   48. 32
49. 17
50. 25 ; 50 ; 75 ; 25
51. 18 ; 30 ; 48 ; 48 – 30 = 18
52. 36 ; 30 ; 66 ; 66 – 30 = 36
53. 38   54. 26
55. 18   56. 9
57. 30   58. 18
59. 4   60. 69
61. 16   62. 27
63. 48   64. 27

3 Addition and Subtraction (2)

Try It
7899

1. 8795   2. 9997
3. 5988   4. 4295
5. 5267   6. 6802
7. 8084   8. 9908
9. 9799   10. 7143
11. 8819   12. 9664
13. 9316   14. 7770
15. 6390   16. 7592
17a. 7553   b. 2010
  c. 6592   d. 2304
  e. 3974   f. 1574

```
  6705      1238      5987
+  848    +  772    +  605
  7553      2010      6592

  2269      3895      1104
+   35    +   79    +  470
  2304      3974      1574
```

18. 8258   19. 7621
20. 6859   21. 4792

22. 1762   23. 8646
24. 3770   25. 2170
26. 2058   27. 7906
28. 8741   29. 2653
30. 3227   31. 1443
32. 262   33. 1767
34. 3458   35. 4782
36. 8056   37. 6564
38a. 2476   b. 1034
  c. 6915   d. 5257
  e. 760   f. 8242
  g. 822   h. 4666

```
   3195       1673
 -  719     -  639
   2476       1034

   7103       6182
 -  188     -  925
   6915       5257

   1004       8995
 -  244     -  753
    760       8242

   1208       5026
 -  386     -  360
    822       4666
```

39. Sum:
```
   4319
 + 2412
   6731
```
Difference:
```
   4319
 - 2412
   1907
```

40. Sum:
```
   3098
 +  976
   4074
```
Difference:
```
   3098
 -  976
   2122
```

41. Sum:
```
   7164
 +  658
   7822
```
Difference:
```
   7164
 -  658
   6506
```

42. Sum:
```
   2156
 +  293
   2449
```
Difference:
```
   2156
 -  293
   1863
```

43. Sum:
```
   6000
 + 3218
   9218
```
Difference:
```
   6000
 - 3218
   2782
```

44.
```
   3245
 + 1623
   4868
```

45.
```
   4085
 + 2169
   6254
```

46.
```
  3219
- 1486
  1733
```

47.
```
  6061
- 2716
  3345
```

4 Multiplication Facts to 81

Try It
24 ; 12 ; 18 ; 24

1. 18
   12 ; 18
2. 28
   14 ; 21 ; 28
3. 30 ; 5 10 15 20 25 30
4. 24 ; 8 16 24
5. 20 ; 4 8 12 16 20
6. 12 ; 2 4 6 8 10 12
7. 64 ; 16 ; 24 ; 32 ; 40 ; 48 ; 56 ; 64
8. 63 ; 9 18 27 36 45 54 63
9. 42 ; 7 14 21 28 35 42
10. 54 ; 6 12 18 24 30 36 42 48 54
11. 18 ; 18
12-16. (Suggested answers)
12. 4 x 4 = 16
    8 x 2 = 16
13. 5 x 2 = 10
    1 x 10 = 10
14. 7 x 3 = 21
    3 x 7 = 21
15. 6 x 2 = 12
    3 x 4 = 12
16. 9 x 2 = 18
    3 x 6 = 18
17a. 12   b. 10   c. 16
   d. 21   e. 15   f. 18
   g. 8   h. 20   i. 18
   j. 28   k. 45   l. 56
   m. 32   n. 54   o. 8
   p. 9   q. 25   r. 48
18. B   19. C
20. A   21. B
22.

X	1	2	3	4	5	6	7	8	9
1	1	2	3	4	5	6	7	8	9
2	2	4	6	8	10	12	14	16	18
3	3	6	9	12	15	18	21	24	27
4	4	8	12	16	20	24	28	32	36
5	5	10	15	20	25	30	35	40	45
6	6	12	18	24	30	36	42	48	54
7	7	14	21	28	35	42	49	56	63
8	8	16	24	32	40	48	56	64	72
9	9	18	27	36	45	54	63	72	81

5 Multiplying 2-digit Numbers

Try It
124

1. 68   2. 66
3. 128   4. 126
5. 90   6. 182
7. 198   8. 225
9. 136   10. 136
11. 99   12. 105
13. 90   14. 174
15. 126   16. 108
17. 276   18. 95
19. 416

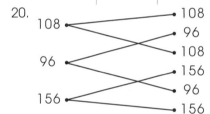

20.
108 •
96 •
156 •
• 108
• 96
• 108
• 156
• 96
• 156

21. 135   22. 216
23. 72   24. 644
25. 252   26. 702
27. 60   28. 140
29. 392   30. 441
31. 165   32. 168
33. 486   34. 335

IT WASN'T RAINING!

35. 12 ; 3 ; 36   36. 24 ; 4 ; 96
    36   96
37. 15 ; 5 ; 75
    75
38. A: $25 ; 4 ; $100
       100
    B: $25 ; 6 ; $150
       150
39. A: 18 ; 3 ; 54
       54
    B: 18 ; 7 ; 126
       126

6 Division Facts to 81

Try It
A ; B

1. 3 ; 3

2. 5 ; 5

3 ; 3

5 ; 5

3. A ; 3 ; 5   D ; 3 ; 7   F ; 2 ; 8
    5 ; 3   7 ; 3   8 ; 2
   E ; 4 ; 6   B ; 4 ; 5   C ; 3 ; 6
    6 ; 4   5 ; 4   6 ; 3

4. Multiplication and division are related because they are inverse operations. This can be seen by rearranging number sentences and swapping the operations. Related facts: 30 ÷ 5 = 6 and 30 ÷ 6 = 5

5. 6 ; 6
6. 8 ; 3 x 8 = 24
7. 6 ; 5 x 6 = 30
8. 8 ; 4 x 8 = 32
9. 8 ; 6 x 8 = 48
10. 3 ; 9 x 3 = 27
11. 5 ; 7 x 5 = 35
12. 6 ; 6 x 6 = 36
13. 7 ; 7
14. 5 ; 45 ÷ 5 = 9
15. 4 ; 32 ÷ 4 = 8
16. 4 ; 28 ÷ 4 = 7
17. 7 ; 21 ÷ 7 = 3
18. 9 ; 54 ÷ 9 = 6
19. 8 ; 40 ÷ 8 = 5
20. 2 ; 16 ÷ 2 = 8
21. 8 ; 72 ÷ 8 = 9
22. (Individual answers)

23a. 54 ÷ 6   b. 40 ÷ 5

     18 ÷ 2   72 ÷ 9

24a. 63 ÷ 9   b. 48 ÷ 8

     21 ÷ 3   24 ÷ 4

25a. 45 ÷ 9   b. 32 ÷ 8

     10 ÷ 2   20 ÷ 5

26a. 27 ÷ 9   b. 18 ÷ 9

     24 ÷ 8   14 ÷ 7

7 Division without Remainders

Try It
dividend ; divisor ; quotient

1. 5
```
      5
3 ) 1 5
    1 5
```

2. 3
```
      3
6 ) 1 8
    1 8
```

3. 3
```
      3
9 ) 2 7
    2 7
```

4. 9
```
      9
5 ) 4 5
    4 5
```

5. 8
```
      8
7 ) 5 6
    5 6
```

6. 4
```
      4
4 ) 1 6
    1 6
```

7.
```
    3          3 7
2 ) 7 4      2 ) 7 4
    6          6
               1 4
    1          1 4
```

8.
```
    1 5
3 ) 4 5
    3
    1 5
    1 5
```

9.
```
    1 3
4 ) 5 2
    4
    1 2
    1 2
```

10.
```
    2 6
3 ) 7 8
    6
    1 8
    1 8
```

11. 21
12. 17
13. 11
14. 15
15. 27
16. 12
17. 14
18. 14
19. 18
```
    2 1          1 7          1 1
3 ) 6 3      5 ) 8 5      6 ) 6 6
    6            5            6
    3            3 5          6
    3            3 5          6
```
```
    1 5          2 7          1 2
5 ) 7 5      2 ) 5 4      8 ) 9 6
    5            4            8
    2 5          1 4          1 6
    2 5          1 4          1 6
```
```
    1 4          1 4          1 8
7 ) 9 8      6 ) 8 4      4 ) 7 2
    7            6            4
    2 8          2 4          3 2
    2 8          2 4          3 2
```

20. 16
21. 12
22. 16
23. 12
24. 11
25. 19
26. 19
27. 16

28. 19
29. A: 14   B: 28
     C: 22   D: 17
     B, C, D, A
30. A: 29   B: 25
     C: 17   D: 16
     A, B, C, D
31. A: 15   B: 13
     C: 36   D: 11
     C, A, B, D

32a.
```
    2 4
2 ) 4 8
    4
    ─
    8
    8
    ─
   24
```
b.
```
    1 6
3 ) 4 8
    3
    ─
    1 8
    1 8
    ──
   16
```
c.
```
    1 2
4 ) 4 8
    4
    ─
    8
    8
    ─
   12
```

33a.
```
    2 0
3 ) 6 0
    6 0
    ──
   20
```
b.
```
    1 5
4 ) 6 0
    4
    ─
    2 0
    2 0
    ──
   15
```
c.
```
    1 2
5 ) 6 0
    5
    ─
    1 0
    1 0
    ──
   12
```

34a.
```
    3 6
2 ) 7 2
    6
    ─
    1 2
    1 2
    ──
   36
```
b.
```
    1 8
4 ) 7 2
    4
    ─
    3 2
    3 2
    ──
   18
```
c.
```
    1 2
6 ) 7 2
    6
    ─
    1 2
    1 2
    ──
   12
```

8 Division with Remainders

Try It

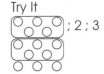 ; 2 ; 3

1. 3 ; 1
2. 2R2
3. 4R2
4. 3R1
5. 6R2
6. 4R2
7. 5R2

8.
```
    7 R1
4 ) 2 9
    2 8
    ──
    1
```
9.
```
    8 R2
5 ) 4 2
    4 0
    ──
    2
```
10.
```
    1 7 R1
2 ) 3 5
    2
    ─
    1 5
    1 4
    ──
    1
```
11.
```
    1 4 R1
4 ) 5 7
    4
    ─
    1 7
    1 6
    ──
    1
```
12. 5 ; 1   13. 4R6   14. 8R1
```
    5 R1          4 R 6          8 R 1
5 ) 2 6       7 ) 3 4        8 ) 6 5
    2 5           2 8            6 4
    ──            ──             ──
    1             6              1
```
15. 14R1   16. 17R1   17. 14R1
```
    1 4 R1        1 7 R1         1 4 R1
3 ) 4 3       3 ) 5 2        2 ) 2 9
    3             3              2
    ─             ─              ─
    1 3           2 2            9
    1 2           2 1            8
    ──            ──             ─
    1             1              1
```
18. 7R4   19. 11R2
20. 10R4   21. 13R4
22. 36R1   23. 7R3
24. 13R3   25. 6R1
26. 12R2   27. 5R3
28.   29.

30.

18 ÷ 4 = 4R2	11 ÷ 5 = 2R2		
36 ÷ 6 = 6	27 ÷ 7 = 3R6		
15 ÷ 2 = 7	54 ÷ 9 = 6	13 ÷ 2 = 6R1	
37 ÷ 5 = 7R1	32 ÷ 4 = 9	21 ÷ 3 = 7	
	35 ÷ 8 = 4R3	43 ÷ 6 = 7R1	
	56 ÷ 7 = 8	24 ÷ 5 = 5R4	
56 ÷ 6 = 9	47 ÷ 9 = 5R2	28 ÷ 3 = 9R1	21 ÷ 8 = 3R3
48 ÷ 5 = 9R2	60 ÷ 7 = 8R4		40 ÷ 6 = 7R2
39 ÷ 9 = 5	90 ÷ 9 = 10		
61 ÷ 8 = 8R1	38 ÷ 4 = 9R2		
41 ÷ 8 = 5R1			

9 Multiplication and Division Facts to 81

Try It
B

1. A   2. B
3. B   4. B
5. B   6. B

7.

8. 5 ; 6 ; 30
   30 ; 5 ; 6
   30 ; 6 ; 5

9. 3 x 7 = 21
   21 ÷ 3 = 7
   21 ÷ 7 = 3

10. 2 x 9 = 18
    18 ÷ 2 = 9
    18 ÷ 9 = 2

11. 48 ÷ 8 = 6
    6 x 8 = 48
    8 x 6 = 48

12. 56 ÷ 8 = 7
    7 x 8 = 56
    8 x 7 = 56

13. 35 ÷ 7 = 5
    5 x 7 = 35
    7 x 5 = 35

14. 4 x 5 = 20
    5 x 4 = 20
    20 ÷ 4 = 5
    20 ÷ 5 = 4

15. 3 x 6 = 18
    6 x 3 = 18
    18 ÷ 3 = 6
    18 ÷ 6 = 3

16. 5 x 7 = 35
    7 x 5 = 35
    35 ÷ 5 = 7
    35 ÷ 7 = 5

17. 6 x 8 = 48
    8 x 6 = 48
    48 ÷ 6 = 8
    48 ÷ 8 = 6

18. 7 x 9 = 63
    9 x 7 = 63
    63 ÷ 7 = 9
    63 ÷ 9 = 7

19. 4 x 9 = 36
    9 x 4 = 36
    36 ÷ 4 = 9
    36 ÷ 9 = 4

20. 42
    6 x 7 = 42
    42 ÷ 6 = 7
    42 ÷ 7 = 6

21. 40
    5 x 8 = 40
    40 ÷ 5 = 8
    40 ÷ 8 = 5

22. 30
    6 x 5 = 30
    30 ÷ 5 = 6
    30 ÷ 6 = 5

23. 36
    4 x 9 = 36
    36 ÷ 4 = 9
    36 ÷ 9 = 4

24. 16
    8 x 2 = 16
    16 ÷ 2 = 8
    16 ÷ 8 = 2

25. 18
    3 x 6 = 18
    18 ÷ 3 = 6
    18 ÷ 6 = 3

26. 9 ; 9
27. 4 ; 4
28. 8 ; 8
29. 5 ; 5
30. 9 ; 9
31. 9 ; 9
32. 7 ; 7
33. 7 ; 7
34. 3 ; 3
35. 3 ; 3
36. 7 ; 7
37. 8 ; 8

38.

START HERE		
9 x 3 = 27 **T**	6 x 5 = 30 **O**	7 + 8 = 15 **P**
9 + 3 = 12 **K**	6 − 5 = 1 **J**	7 x 8 = 56 **Y**
3 x 9 = 27 **H**	30 ÷ 5 = 6 **N**	56 ÷ 7 = 8 **W**
27 ÷ 3 = 9 **E**	5 x 6 = 30 **L**	8 x 7 = 56 **A**

35 ÷ 5 = 7 **R**	6 x 7 = 42 **L**	8 + 5 = 13 **Q**
7 x 5 = 35 **N**	6 x 1 = 6 **I**	8 x 5 = 40 **Y**
5 x 2 = 10 **S**	42 ÷ 6 = 7 **E**	40 ÷ 8 = 5 **T**
5 x 7 = 35 **M**	42 ÷ 7 = 6 **A**	40 ÷ 5 = 8 **O**

8 x 6 = 48 **A**	3 x 7 = 21 **D**	9 x 8 = 72 **A**
48 ÷ 3 = 16 **T**	21 ÷ 7 = 3 **O**	8 + 9 = 17 **X**
48 ÷ 8 = 6 **T**	7 + 3 = 10 **V**	8 x 9 = 72 **T**
6 x 8 = 48 **H**	7 x 3 = 21 **M**	72 ÷ 8 = 9 **H**

THE ONLY WAY TO LEARN MATH IS TO DO MATH!

10 Multiplication and Division (1)

Try It
50 ; 500 ; 5000

1. 10 ; 20 ; 30 ; 40 ; 50 ; 60 ; 70 ; 80 ; 90 ; 100
2. 100 ; 200 ; 300 ; 400 ; 500 ; 600 ; 700 ; 800 ; 900 ; 1000
3. 1000 ; 2000 ; 3000 ; 4000 ; 5000 ; 6000 ; 7000 ; 8000 ; 9000 ; 10 000
4. 300
5. 4000
6. 70 000
7. 1000
8. 200
9. 70 000
10. 80 000
11. 9000
12. 10
13. 7
14. 800
15. 100
16. 100
17. 300
18. 1000
19. 10
20. 2 ; 40 ; 90 ; 6 ; 80 ; 100 ; 700 ; 9000 ; 7
21. 8 ; 90 ; 400 ; 50 ; 6000
22. 2000
23. 70 000
24. 60
25. 9
26. 70
27. 4000
28. 80
29. 50 000
30. 300
31. 1000
32. 700
33. 20 000

34.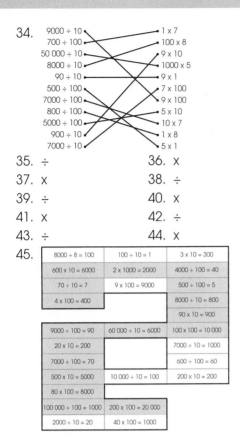

9000 ÷ 10	1 x 7
700 ÷ 100	100 x 8
50 000 ÷ 10	9 x 10
8000 ÷ 10	1000 x 5
90 ÷ 10	9 x 1
500 ÷ 100	7 x 100
7000 ÷ 100	9 x 100
800 ÷ 100	5 x 10
5000 ÷ 100	10 x 7
900 ÷ 10	1 x 8
7000 ÷ 10	5 x 1

35. ÷   36. x
37. x   38. ÷
39. ÷   40. x
41. x   42. ÷
43. ÷   44. x

45.

8000 ÷ 8 = 100	100 ÷ 10 = 1	3 x 10 = 300
600 x 10 = 6000	2 x 1000 = 2000	4000 ÷ 100 = 40
70 ÷ 10 = 7	9 x 100 = 9000	500 ÷ 100 = 5
4 x 100 = 400		8000 ÷ 10 = 800
		90 x 10 = 900
9000 ÷ 100 = 90	60 000 ÷ 10 = 6000	100 x 100 = 10 000
20 x 10 = 200		7000 ÷ 10 = 1000
7000 ÷ 100 = 70		600 ÷ 100 = 60
500 x 10 = 5000	10 000 ÷ 10 = 100	200 x 10 = 200
80 x 100 = 8000		
100 000 ÷ 100 = 1000	200 x 100 = 20 000	
2000 ÷ 10 = 20	40 x 100 = 1000	

11 Multiplication and Division (2)

Try It

	1	2
x		3
	3	6

; 36

1.
```
   21
 x  4
   84
```
84

2.
```
   32
 x  3
   96
```
96

3.
```
   16
 x  6
   96
```
96

4.
```
   19
 x  5
   95
```
95

5.
```
   35
 x  4
  140
```
140

6.
```
   43
 x  4
  172
```
172

7.
```
   26
 x  9
  234
```
234

8.
```
   18
 x  3
   54
```
54

9.
```
   32
 x  9
  288
```
288

10. 9   11. 15
12. 13   13. 11
14. 15   15. 13
16. 14   17. 27
18. 13

```
      9
  8)7 2
    7 2
```

```
    1 5
  3)4 5
    3
    1 5
    1 5
```

```
    1 3
  4)5 2
    4
    1 2
    1 2
```

```
    1 1
  9)9 9
    9
    9
    9
```

```
    1 5
  4)6 0
    4
    2 0
    2 0
```

```
    1 3
  7)9 1
    7
    2 1
    2 1
```

```
    1 4
  5)7 0
    5
    2 0
    2 0
```

```
    2 7
  3)8 1
    6
    2 1
    2 1
```

```
    1 3
  2)2 6
    2
    6
    6
```

19a. 30   b. 12
c. 23   d. 125
e. 29   f. 13
g. 104   h. 136
i. 19   j. 140

33	17	49	50	23
83	92	53	88	125
12	140	30	19	29
104	5	28	100	25
13	91	81	20	111
136	27	35	16	46

20. 80 ; 800 ; 8000
21. 290 ; 2900 ; 29 000
22. 300 ; 3000 ; 30 000
23. 150 ; 1500 ; 15 000
24. 0 ; 0 ; 0
25. 10 ; 100 ; 1000

26.

÷ 10	÷ 100
20	2
300	30
90	9
6000	600
50	5
700	70
10 000	1000
200	20
80	8

27.

÷ 10	÷ 100
130	13
4200	420
510	51
99 100	9910
370	37
9800	980
2510	251
46 980	4698
10 110	1011

28. A ; B ; E ; D   29. A ; D ; F ; B ; E

12 Fractions

Try It
two fourths

1. three eighths
2. two fifths
3. one fourth
4. four sevenths
5. three sixths
6. five tenths

7-9. (Suggested colouring)

7. 8. 9.

10. $\frac{2}{4}$ 11. $\frac{3}{5}$ 12. $\frac{2}{3}$ 13. $\frac{4}{6}$

14. $\frac{3}{6}$ 15. $\frac{2}{4}$ 16. $\frac{4}{8}$ 17. $\frac{1}{5}$

18. $\frac{3}{7}$ 19. $\frac{2}{3}$ 20. $\frac{5}{9}$ 21. $\frac{8}{10}$

22. A: $\frac{3}{5}$ B: $\frac{2}{4}$ C: $\frac{1}{3}$

   D: $\frac{2}{8}$ E: $\frac{1}{2}$ F: $\frac{2}{9}$

23. 24. 25.

26. 27. 28.

29. 30. 31.

32.  ; ✔ 33. ; ✔

34.  ; <

35. 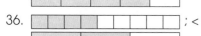 ; >

36. 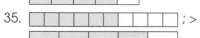 ; <

37. 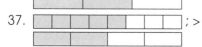 ; >

13 Decimals

Try It
0.2

1. 0.9 2. 1.5
3. 0.4 4. 1.3
5. 1.8 6. 2.2
7. A: 0.5 B: 0.8
   C: 0.6 D: 0.6
   E: 1.4 F: 2.4

8. 9. 10.

---

11. 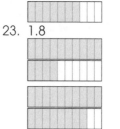 12.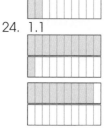

13.
   1.5
   1.2 1.3 1.4 1.5 1.6 1.7 1.8 1.9

14.
   2.2
   1.7 1.8 1.9 2 2.1 2.2 2.3 2.4

15.
   3.1
   2.8 2.9 3 3.1 3.2 3.3 3.4 3.5

16.
   4.5
   3.9 4 4.1 4.2 4.3 4.4 4.5 4.6

17.
   5.7
   5.4 5.5 5.6 5.7 5.8 5.9 6 6.1

18. <
   0.8 1.2
   0   1   2

19. <
   1.7   2.9
   1.5   2.5   3.5

20. < ; >
   1.8 2.1   2.9 3.2
   1   2   3   4

21. 0.7 22. 0.8

23. 1.8 24. 1.1

25a. 0.7 b. 1.5 c. 4.3
   d. 2 e. 1.3 f. 2.7
26a. 0.3 b. 0.5 c. 2.3
   d. 1.3 e. 2.2 f. 3.5
27. < 28. < 29. >
30. > 31. > 32. >
33. < 34. > 35. <
36a. 0.2, 0.3, 1.1, 1.3
   b. 2.3, 2.4, 3.2, 4.3
37a. 2.5, 1.3, 1, 0.8
   b. 3.5, 3.1, 1.5, 1.3

14 Fractions and Decimals

Try It
$\frac{6}{10}$; 0.6

1. $\frac{4}{10}$; 0.4 2. $\frac{5}{10}$; 0.5 3. $\frac{6}{10}$; 0.6

4. $\frac{3}{10}$; 0.3 5. $\frac{8}{10}$; 0.8 6. $\frac{2}{10}$; 0.2

7. A: $\frac{9}{10}$; 0.9 B: $\frac{1}{10}$; 0.1 C: $\frac{7}{10}$; 0.7

8. six tenths ; $\frac{6}{10}$

9. five tenths ; $\frac{5}{10}$

10. nine tenths ; $\frac{9}{10}$

11. $\frac{2}{10}$; 0.2

12. $\frac{8}{10}$; 0.8

13. $\frac{4}{10}$; 0.4

14. $\frac{5}{10}$; 0.5

15. $\frac{6}{10}$; 0.6

16. $\frac{7}{10}$; 0.7

17. $\frac{1}{5}$; 0.2

18. $\frac{1}{2}$; 0.5

19. $\frac{4}{5}$; 0.8

20. $\frac{2}{5}$; 0.4

21. $2\frac{6}{10}$; 2.6

22. $1\frac{7}{10}$; 1.7

23. $3\frac{4}{5}$; 3.8

24. $2\frac{1}{2}$; 2.5

25. $2\frac{2}{5}$; 2.4

26. $3\frac{3}{10}$; 3.3

27. $3\frac{1}{2}$; 3.5

28a. 0.1
b. 0.4
c. 0.5
d. 1.3
e. 2.8

29a. $\frac{6}{10}$
b. $\frac{8}{10}$
c. $\frac{9}{10}$
d. $1\frac{5}{10}$
e. $1\frac{4}{10}$

15 Length

Try It
cm

1. A: cm   B: mm   C: dm
   D: m   E: cm   F: mm
   G: km   H: dm   I: m

2. purple   green   blue   red

3. A: 8 cm ; 80 mm   B: 5 cm ; 50 mm
   C: 7 cm ; 70 mm   D: 9 cm ; 90 mm
   E: 6 cm ; 60 mm   F: 3 cm ; 30 mm

4a. A   b. B
5a. B   b. A   c. A
6a. A   b. B   c. B
7a. B   b. A   c. A
8. 60   9. 30   10. 300   11. 9000
12. 70   13. 20   14. 4   15. 8000
16. 5   17. 90
18. A: 300 mm ; 30   B: 2 km ; 2000
    C: 12 m ; 1200   D: 4000 cm ; 40
    E: 60 mm ; 6   F: 700 cm ; 7
    G: 1300 mm ; 130   H: 2000 m ; 2
    I: 2 m ; 200

16 Perimeter

Try It
8

1. 8   2. 10 cm   3. 8 cm
4. 10 cm   5. 12 cm
6. 12 cm ; 12 cm ; 14 cm ; 18 cm

a.
b.   c.

7. 3 ; 3 ; 3 ; 3 ; 12
8. 2 + 4 + 2 + 4 ; 12
9. 4 + 1 + 4 + 1 ; 10

10. A: 3 ; 4 ; 5 ; 12
    B: 5 + 5 + 5 + 5 = 20 (cm)
    C: 3 + 3 + 5 = 11 (cm)
    D: 2 + 4 + 4 + 2 = 12 (cm)
    E: 5 + 5 + 2 = 12 (cm)
    F: 3 + 5 + 3 + 5 = 16 (cm)

11.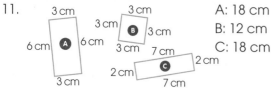

    A: 18 cm
    B: 12 cm
    C: 18 cm

12. 21 cm ; 22 cm ; 6 cm ; 13 cm

17 Mass

Try It
kg

1. mg ; kg ; mg ; g ; kg ; kg
2. 7 g ; 50 mg ; 300 mg
   2 kg ; 10 kg ; 200 mg
   300 g ; 5 g ; 800 kg
3. 3000 ; 2000 ; 10 000 ; 5 ; 8 ; 4
4. 6000 ; 4000 ; 3000 ; 7 ; 9 ; 4
5. 8000   6. 2000
7. 40 000   8. 3
9. 40   10. 300 000
11. 2   12. 15 000
13a. 2 kg   b. 5000 mg
14a. 4 kg   b. 7 g
15. 30 mg ; 300 mg ; 3 g
16. 4000 mg ; 40 g ; 4 kg
17. 80 kg ; 800 g ; 8000 mg
18. 20 000 g ; 2 kg ; 200 mg
19. (Suggested drawing)

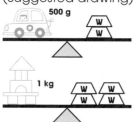

20a. 4 weights   b. 12 weights
21. 2 toy cars
22. A: 500   B: 2   C: 250
    D: 1500   E: 850

18 Time

Try It
day ; week ; year

1. A   2. B   3. B
4. A   5. B   6. A
7. A   8. B   9. B
10. A   11. A   12. 120
13. 180   14. 144   15. 3
16. 600   17. 480   18. 2
19. 4   20. 2   21. 21
22. 4   23. 24   24. 208
25. 49   26. 2   27. 3
28. 35   29. 2   30. 40
31. 300   32. 50   33. 60
34. 100   35. 70   36. 500
37. A: 5:20   B: 12:30
    C: 7:35   D: 10:10
    E: 1:50   F: 6:40
    G: 3:15   H: 9:55
38.

39a.

FEBRUARY 2020						
SUN	MON	TUE	WED	THU	FRI	SAT
						1
2	③	4	5	6	7	8
9	10	11	12	13	14	⑮
16	17	18	19	20	21	22
23	24	25	26	27	28	㉙

MARCH 2020						
SUN	MON	TUE	WED	THU	FRI	SAT
1	2	3	4	5	6	⑦
8	9	10	11	12	13	14
⑮	16	17	18	19	20	21
22	23	24	㉕	26	27	28
29	30	31				

APRIL 2020						
SUN	MON	TUE	WED	THU	FRI	SAT
			1	2	3	4
⑤	6	7	8	9	10	11
12	13	14	15	16	17	18
19	20	21	22	㉓	24	25
㉖	27	28	29	30		

b. April 1, 2020
   February 14, 2020
   March 24, 2020
c. Tuesday ; Thursday ; Saturday

19 Shapes

Try It

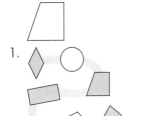

1.

rhombus
trapezoid
rectangle
square
kite
parallelogram

2.

3.

4.

5.

equal sides	parallel sides	right angle	line of symmetry
✔	✔	✔	✔
✔	✔	✔	✔
✔	✔		
✔	✔		✔
✔			✔
✔	✔		✔

6. 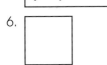   7.

4 ; 2 ; 4 ; 4   2 ; 0 ; 0 ; 1

8.

4 ; 2 ; 0 ; 2

9. F   10. T   11. F
12. T   13. T   14. T
15-17. (Suggested drawings)

15.   16.   17.

square   kite   rectangle or
                               rhombus

20 Solids

Try It

1.

triangular prism

2.

rectangular pyramid

3.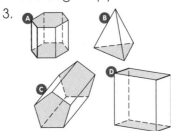

A: hexagonal prism
B: triangular pyramid
C: pentagonal prism
D: rectangular prism

4. E ; 5 ; 5 ; 8
5. C ; 5 ; 6 ; 9
6. A ; 6 ; 6 ; 10
7. D ; 6 ; 8 ; 12
8. B ; 4 ; 4 ; 6
9. F ; 7 ; 10 ; 15

10.

Solid
G
B
A, B, D, E, G
A, B, D, E, G
D, G, H
D, G

a. A, B, E, G, I
b. F, I
c. D
d. C, F

11-14. (Suggested drawings)

11. rectangular prism

12. pentagonal pyramid

13. triangular pyramid

14. cube

15. pentagonal pyramid
16. rectangular prism and cube

21 Grid Maps

Try It

leaf

1a. apple ; orange ; pear ; lemon
 b. D7 ; B8 ; F5 ; G8
2a. A10, B5, C13, D3, E9, G6, H1, H14
 b.

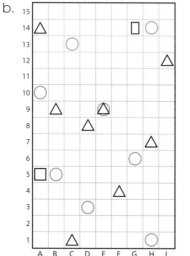

 c. E9   d. H1, H14
3a. circle   b. H14
4a. circle   b. B5

5a.

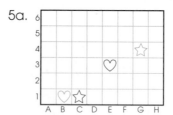

 b. E3 ; C1
6a. 3 squares to the right and 1 square down
 b. He goes 1 square to the right and 2 squares down.
 c. He goes 1 square to the right and 4 squares down.
 d. He should go 4 squares to the right and 1 square up.

7.

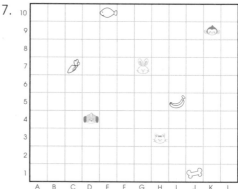

 a. 4 squares to the left
 b. The monkey goes 2 squares to the left and 4 squares down to reach the banana.
 c. The cat goes 3 squares to the left and 7 squares up to reach the fish.
 d. The dog goes 6 squares to the right and 3 squares down to reach the bone.

22 Reflections

Try It

1. A ; B ; D : F : H
2.

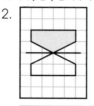

3.

4.

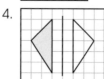

5.

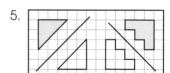

6.

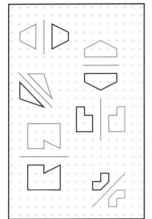

7a. A   b. in Line B

c.

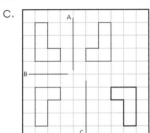

8.

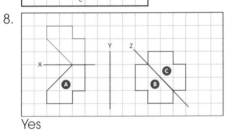

Yes

23   Data Management

Try It

4 ; 4

1. 5 ; 5   2. 5 ; 2   3. 3 ; 3

4. 11 ; 10   5. 5 ; 5, 7   6. 10 ; 9, 11

7. 4 ; 5   8. 3 ; 2, 4

9. 3, 3, 4, 4, 4, 5, 6

    4 ; 4

10. 1, 1, 1, 3, 4, 6, 8, 8, 9

    4 ; 1

11. 5, 6, 6, 6, 7, 10, 10

    6 ; 6

12. 4, 4, 9, 9, 9, 12, 12

    9 ; 9

13. D ; B ; A ; C   14. 2 ; 2

15. 15 trees ; 15 trees

16. 13 apples ; 12 apples

17. 15 kg ; 15 kg

18. 84 points ; 74 and 86 points

19. 1 kg ; 2 kg ; 3 kg

20. 2 kg ; 2 kg

21. 4   22. 12   23. 16   24. 9

1   Addition and Subtraction

Try It

$$\begin{array}{r} 2817 \\ -\ \ 352 \\ \hline 2465 \end{array}$$

1a. 7073

$$\begin{array}{r} 6548 \\ +\ \ 525 \\ \hline 7073 \end{array}$$

b. 1579

$$\begin{array}{r} 1160 \\ +\ \ 419 \\ \hline 1579 \end{array}$$

c. 4719

$$\begin{array}{r} 4182 \\ +\ \ 537 \\ \hline 4719 \end{array}$$

d. 6063

$$\begin{array}{r} 5755 \\ +\ \ 308 \\ \hline 6063 \end{array}$$

2a. 6158

$$\begin{array}{r} 6721 \\ -\ \ 563 \\ \hline 6158 \end{array}$$

b. 8179

$$\begin{array}{r} 8464 \\ -\ \ 285 \\ \hline 8179 \end{array}$$

c. 6789

$$\begin{array}{r} 7641 \\ -\ \ 852 \\ \hline 6789 \end{array}$$

d. 2089

$$\begin{array}{r} 2586 \\ -\ \ 497 \\ \hline 2089 \end{array}$$

3. 3600

   4110

   4820

   3718

   3800

   1020

   3792

   3769

   2778

   4002

   3021

   1114

$$\begin{array}{r} 4800 \\ -\ 1200 \\ \hline 3600 \end{array} \qquad \begin{array}{r} 5360 \\ -\ 1250 \\ \hline 4110 \end{array}$$

$$\begin{array}{r} 2317 \\ +\ 2503 \\ \hline 4820 \end{array} \qquad \begin{array}{r} 2425 \\ +\ 1293 \\ \hline 3718 \end{array}$$

$$\begin{array}{r} 5000 \\ -\ 1200 \\ \hline 3800 \end{array} \qquad \begin{array}{r} 2600 \\ -\ 1580 \\ \hline 1020 \end{array}$$

$$\begin{array}{r} 2367 \\ +\ 1425 \\ \hline 3792 \end{array} \qquad \begin{array}{r} 5123 \\ -\ 1354 \\ \hline 3769 \end{array}$$

$$\begin{array}{r} 4444 \\ -\ 1666 \\ \hline 2778 \end{array} \qquad \begin{array}{r} 2008 \\ +\ 1994 \\ \hline 4002 \end{array}$$

$$\begin{array}{r} 2463 \\ +\ \ 558 \\ \hline 3021 \end{array} \qquad \begin{array}{r} 889 \\ +\ 225 \\ \hline 1114 \end{array}$$

Math is such fun!

4. 4597 ;
```
  4597
– 1380
  3217
```

5. 1588 ;
```
  1588
+ 4192
  5780
```

6. 6403 ;
```
  6403
– 2794
  3609
```

7. 5320 ;
```
  5320
– 3493
  1827
```

8. 5585 ;
```
  5585
+ 1436
  7021
```

9. A: ✔
   B: ✘ ; 3217
   C: ✘ ; 9172
   D: ✔
   E: ✘ ; 6021
   F: ✔
   G: ✘ ; 5120
   H: ✘ ; 2911
   I: ✔
   J: ✔

10. 4313 ;
```
  2800
+ 1500
  4300
```

11. 2108 ;
```
  3000
–  900
  2100
```

12. 4824 ;
```
  8100
– 3300
  4800
```

13. 5716 ;
```
  2400
+ 3300
  5700
```

14. 6280 ;
```
  4600
+ 1700
  6300
```

15. 3200 ; 1900
    Estimate: 3200 ; 1900 ; 5100
    Actual: 3217 ; 1948 ; 5165
    Estimate: 3200 ; 1900 ; 1300
    Actual: 3217 ; 1948 ; 1269

16. 1400 ; 5600
    Estimate: 1400 + 5600 = 7000
    Actual: 1425 + 5577 = 7002
    Estimate: 5600 – 1400 = 4200
    Actual: 5577 – 1425 = 4152

2   Multiplication

Try It
0 ; 21
19 ; 36

1. 0 ; 42 ; 20 ; 0 ; 0 ; 0 ; 45 ; 32 ; 0 ; 63 ; 0
   24 ; 0 ; 34 ; 40 ; 0 ; 0 ; 82 ; 0
   0 ; 18 ; 13 ; 0 ; 0 ; 16 ; 0 ; 69

2. Level 1: 2 ; 12 ; 0 ; 5 ; 12 ; 4 ; 0 ; 3 ; 20 ; 14
   Level 2: 24 ; 35 ; 54 ; 9 ; 32 ; 0 ; 27 ; 24 ; 40 ; 21
   Level 3: 63 ; 64 ; 81 ; 48 ; 56 ; 36 ; 49 ; 45 ; 35 ; 40

3. 136
4. 69
5. 288
6. 56
7. 399
8. 432
9. 360
10. 195
11. 201
12. 368
13. 108
14. 385
15. 273
16. 180
17. 132
18. 729
19. 208
20. 210
21. 336
22. 567
23. 380
24. 182 ; 112 ; 198
    95 ; 144 ; 336
    162 ; 110 ; 651

237	98	333	450	198
519	702	681	382	112
451	486	95	144	110
64	509	182	514	641
913	972	162	633	87
167	286	651	706	381
99	201	336	600	101

25a. 9   b. 54   c. 108
26a. 0   b. 96   c. 216
27a. 16   b. 40   c. 96

3 Division

Try It

17 ; 0

23 ; 0

1. 0
2. 23
3. 0
4. 40
5. 0
6. 13
7. 0
8. 19
9. 0
10. 52
11. 0
12. 11
13. 1
14. 0
15. 8
16. 1
17. 0
18. 1
19. 4
20. 1
21. 0
22. 21
23. 0
24. 1

25.
```
      2 1
  3 ) 6 3
      6
      ─
        3
        3
        ─
```

26.
```
      1 9 R3
  4 ) 7 9
      4
      ─
      3 9
      3 6
      ───
        3
```

27.
```
      1 9 R1
  3 ) 5 8
      3
      ─
      2 8
      2 7
      ───
        1
```

28.
```
      2 1 R1
  2 ) 4 3
      4
      ─
        3
        2
        ─
        1
```

29.
```
      1 2
  7 ) 8 4
      7
      ─
      1 4
      1 4
      ───
```

30.
```
      1 3 R1
  3 ) 4 0
      3
      ─
      1 0
        9
        ─
        1
```

31.
```
      1 4
  6 ) 8 4
      6
      ─
      2 4
      2 4
      ───
```

32.
```
      1 9 R2
  5 ) 9 7
      5
      ─
      4 7
      4 5
      ───
        2
```

33. 12
34. 9R3
35. 13
36. 14R1
37. 11R2
38. 14R1
39. 15R1
40. 30R1
41. 8R2
42. 13R4
43. 11R4

44.
D:
```
        3 R1
  7 ) 2 2
      2 1
      ───
        1
```
A:
```
      1 2 R3
  8 ) 9 9
      8
      ─
      1 9
      1 6
      ───
        3
```
S:
```
        6 R1
  9 ) 5 5
      5 4
      ───
        1
```

S:
```
      1 7 R3
  5 ) 8 8
      5
      ─
      3 8
      3 5
      ───
        3
```
E:
```
      2 8 R1
  3 ) 8 5
      6
      ─
      2 5
      2 4
      ───
        1
```
R:
```
      1 4 R1
  5 ) 7 1
      5
      ─
      2 1
      2 0
      ───
        1
```

D:
```
      1 2 R5
  6 ) 7 7
      6
      ─
      1 7
      1 2
      ───
        5
```
R:
```
      1 4 R1
  4 ) 5 7
      4
      ─
      1 7
      1 6
      ───
        1
```
S:
```
        8 R1
  8 ) 6 5
      6 4
      ───
        1
```

O:
```
      1 1 R2
  3 ) 3 5
      3
      ─
        5
        3
        ─
        2
```
E:
```
      2 3 R1
  2 ) 4 7
      4
      ─
        7
        6
        ─
        1
```
P:
```
        8
  7 ) 5 6
      5 6
      ───
```

DRESSER

45. 1: ✔

2: ✗ ; 16R2

3: ✔

4: ✔

5: ✗ ; 8R4

6: ✔

7: ✔

8: ✔

9: ✔

10: ✗ ; 15R4

11: ✔

12: ✔

13: ✔

14: ✔

15: ✔

16: ✔

17: ✗ ; 17

18: ✔

19: ✔
20: ✔
16

4 Multiplication and Division

Try It

```
    34
 x   2
─────────
    68
```
correct

1. ✔ ;
```
      3 7
   2│7 4
     6
    ─────
     1 4
     1 4
```

2. ✗ ;
```
        1 3
     x   7
   ─────────
        9 1
```

3. ✔ ;
```
      1 6
   4│6 4
     4
    ─────
     2 4
     2 4
```

4. ✔ ;
```
        2 7
     x   3
   ─────────
        8 1
```

5. ✗ ;
```
      2 2 R 1
   3│6 7
     6
    ─────
       7
       6
    ─────
       1
```

6. ✔ ;
```
        1 8
     x   4
   ─────────
        7 2
```

7. 46
8. 16
9. 36
10. 99
11. 17
12. 96
13. 14
14. 72
15. 12
16. 115
17. 84
18. 63
19. 12
20. 17
21. 54
22. 14
23. 23
24. 95
25. 84
26. 21
27. 104

28a. ✔
12 x 5 = 60
60 + 2 = 62

b. ✗
6 x 7 = 42
42 + 5 = 47

c. ✔
18 x 3 = 54
54 + 2 = 56

d. ✔
13 x 7 = 91
91 + 1 = 92

e. ✔
13 x 6 = 78
78 + 5 = 83

f. ✔
4 x 9 = 36
36 + 5 = 41

g. ✗
5 x 7 = 35
35 + 4 = 39

h. ✔
15 x 5 = 75
75 + 1 = 76

i. ✔
8 x 8 = 64
64 + 5 = 69

j. ✗
14 x 4 = 56
56 + 2 = 58

k. ✗
11 x 6 = 66
66 + 5 = 71

29.
```
      1 2 R 3
   6│7 5
     6
    ─────
     1 5
     1 2
    ─────
       3
```
12 x 6 = 72
72 + 3 = 75

30.
```
      1 4 R 1
   2│2 9
     2
    ─────
       9
       8
    ─────
       1
```
14 x 2 = 28
28 + 1 = 29

31.
```
      1 8 R 2
   3│5 6
     3
    ─────
     2 6
     2 4
    ─────
       2
```
18 x 3 = 54
54 + 2 = 56

32. 24 x 3 = 72
```
      2 4
   3│7 2
     6
    ─────
     1 2
     1 2
```
72

33. 68 ÷ 4 = 17
```
        1 7
     x   4
   ─────────
        6 8
```
17

34. 38 ÷ 3 = 12R2
12 x 3 = 36
36 + 2 = 38
12 ; 2

5 Fractions

Try It
$\frac{1}{2}$

1. $\frac{1}{3}$
2. $\frac{2}{3}$
3. $\frac{2}{4}$
4. $\frac{1}{2}$
5. $\frac{4}{6}$
6. $\frac{3}{4}$

7. A: $\frac{2}{3}$ B: $\frac{1}{4}$

   C: $\frac{1}{2}$ D: $\frac{1}{3}$

   E: $\frac{1}{2}$ F: $\frac{1}{6}$

8.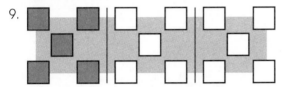

9.

10.

11.

12.

13.

14. >   15. <

16. >   17. >

18. <   19. >

20. <   21. >

22. <   23. >

24. <   25. <

26. <   27. >

28. $\frac{2}{5}$; $\frac{3}{5}$; $\frac{4}{5}$; $\frac{5}{5}$

29. $\frac{0}{8} < \frac{1}{8} < \frac{5}{8} < \frac{9}{8}$

30. $\frac{3}{10} < \frac{4}{10} < \frac{7}{10} < \frac{9}{10}$

31. $\frac{1}{9} < \frac{2}{9} < \frac{4}{9} < \frac{11}{9}$

32. $\frac{2}{8} < \frac{6}{8} < \frac{7}{8} < \frac{8}{8}$

33. $\frac{0}{7} < \frac{1}{7} < \frac{4}{7} < \frac{8}{7}$

34.

35.

36.

6 Decimals

Try It

0.6

1. 0.5

2. 0.8

3. 1.1

4. 1.2

5. 1.9

6. 2.5

7. 0.7   8. 1.8

9. 1.1   10. 1.3

11. 2.3   12. 2.3

13. 3.0   14. 3.4

15. 4.1

16. 0.9 ; 0.9   17. 1.5

$$\begin{array}{r} 1.1 \\ +\ 0.4 \\ \hline 1.5 \end{array}$$

18. 3.1   19. 3.3

$$\begin{array}{r} 1.8 \\ +\ 1.3 \\ \hline 3.1 \end{array} \qquad \begin{array}{r} 0.9 \\ +\ 2.4 \\ \hline 3.3 \end{array}$$

20. 2.2   21. 4.2

$$\begin{array}{r} 0.5 \\ +\ 1.7 \\ \hline 2.2 \end{array} \qquad \begin{array}{r} 1.4 \\ +\ 2.8 \\ \hline 4.2 \end{array}$$

22. 4.2

$$\begin{array}{r} 0.7 \\ +\ 3.5 \\ \hline 4.2 \end{array}$$

23.
1.5

24.
1.3

25.
0.7

26.
0.5

27.
0.9

28.
0.8

29. 1.1   30. 1.4
31. 2.2   32. 1.6
33. 0.4   34. 0.9
35. 1.8
36. 1.4
    2.6
  − 1.2
    1.4
37. 2.2
    6.8
  − 4.6
    2.2
38. 2.8
    5.4
  − 2.6
    2.8
39. 1.1
    3.6
  − 2.5
    1.1
40. 0.7
    1.5
  − 0.8
    0.7

41. 0.2
    6.1
  − 5.9
    0.2
42. 1.9
    4.3
  − 2.4
    1.9
43. 0.9
    2.5
  − 1.6
    0.9
44. 0.9
    3.3
  − 2.4
    0.9
45. A: 3.6
    B: 2.3
    C: 3.5
    D: 0.9
    E: 3.7
    F: 4.1
    G: 2.8
    H: 6.2

2.4 + 1.2 3.6	3.6 − 1.3 2.3	3.0 + 0.5 3.5	1.0 − 0.1 0.9
5.0 − 1.3 3.7	2.7 + 1.4 4.1	4.0 − 1.2 2.8	3.3 + 2.9 6.2

7 Money

Try It
$55.75

1. $44
2. $42.40
3. $86.10

4a.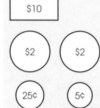

b.

c.

$2 $1

25¢ 25¢ 25¢

d.

$1 25¢ 25¢ 25¢

5. 5 ; 35 ; $5.35
6. 1 ; 15 ; $1.15
7. 8 ; 10 ; $8.10
8. 5 ; 75 ; $5.75
9. Sum: $10.75

dollar	cent
6	25
+ 4	50
10	75

Difference: $1.75

dollar	cent
6	25
− 4	50
1	75

10. Sum: $12.05

dollar	cent
10	70
+ 1	35
12	05

Difference: $9.35

dollar	cent
10	70
− 1	35
9	35

11. Sum: $9.50

dollar	cent
8	00
+ 1	50
9	50

Difference: $6.50

dollar	cent
8	00
− 1	50
6	50

12a.

dollar	cent
20	15
+ 22	50
42	65

$42.65

b.

dollar	cent
11	90
+ 10	95
22	85

$22.85

13a.

dollar	cent
11	90
− 10	95
	95

$0.95

b.

dollar	cent
22	50
− 20	15
2	35

$2.35

14a.

dollar	cent
50	00
− 20	15
29	85

$29.85

b.

dollar	cent
50	00
− 22	50
27	50

$27.50

8 Area

Try It

6

1. 6   2. 7
3. 6   4. 6
5a. 6 ; 4 ; 16
   b.

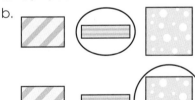

c. (Suggested drawings)

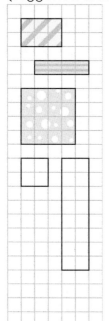

6a. 6 ; 5 ; 8 ; 5 ; 7

b-d.

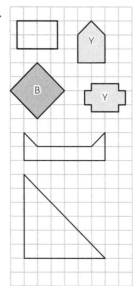

7. 4 ; 2 ; 8
8. 4 ; 3 ; 12
9. yes
10. A: 18
    B: 9 square centimetres
    C: 12 square centimetres

9 Capacity and Volume

Try It

L

1. mL: A, B, D, F
   L: C, E, G, H
2. 300 mL

3. 100 mL
4. 50 L
5. 300 L
6. 3000 ; 6000 ; 4000 ; 10 000 ; 9000
7. 7 ; 8 ; 5 ; 20 ; 12
8. 1 L: 10 ; 4 ; 2
   2 L: 20 ; 8 ; 4
9. A: 5
   B: 5 cubic centimetres
   C: 6 cubic centimetres
   D: 5 cubic centimetres
   E: 5 cubic centimetres
   F: 9 cubic centimetres

10-11. (Suggested drawings)

10. 6   11. 7

12a. volume   b. capacity
  c. capacity   d. volume
  e. capacity   f. volume
13. 20 ; 240   14. mL ; 15

10 Time

Try It
March April May June July
1   2   3   4
4 months

1. 5 days
2. 3 days
3. 4 months
4. 8 months
5. 5 years
6. 5 years
7. 3 days
8. 9 months
9. 4 days
10. 10 months
11. 3 days
12. 2 years
13. 4 months
14a. 7 days
  b. 3 days
  c. 6 days
  d. 33 days

15a. April 17
  b. May 3
  c. May 17
  d. June 15
16a. April 3
  b. April 7
  c. June 17
17. 20 minutes
18. 35 minutes
19. 15 minutes
20. 20 minutes
21. 35 minutes
22. 35 minutes
23a. 40 minutes
  b. 35 minutes
  c. 25 minutes
  d. 50 minutes
24. 0 ; 40
25. 2 hours 25 minutes
26a. 10 minutes
  b. 10 minutes
  c. 30 minutes
27. 35 minutes
28. no
29. 10 minutes
30.

Math class	English class	recess starts	recess ends
9:00	9:50	10:40	10:55 11:00

31. 5 hours 40 minutes

11 Angles

Try It

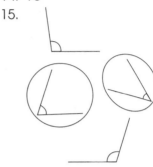

1.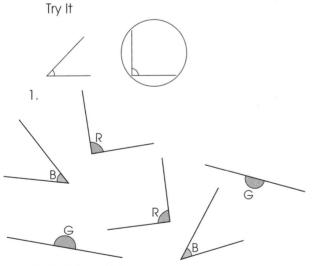

2. A: right angle
   B: straight angle
   C: half a right angle
   D: right angle

E: straight angle
F: half a right angle
3. smaller
4. smaller ; greater
5. 90°
6. 45°
7. 45°
8. 180°
9. 90°
10. 180°
11. 45°
12. 180°
13. 45°
14. 90°
15.

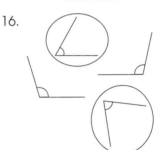

16.

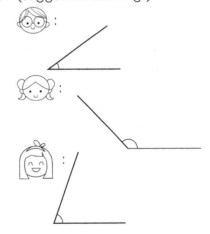

17. (Suggested drawings)

 :

 :

:

18.

smallest	largest

12 Solids

Try It

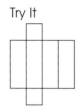

1. C ; D ; A ; B

2.   3.

4. A ; cube

5.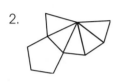

cube

6.

rectangular pyramid

7.

triangular pyramid

8.

hexagonal prism

9.

B A C

10.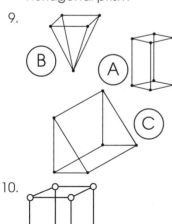

11.

12.

13.

triangular pyramid

14.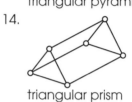

triangular prism

15.

pentagonal pyramid

13 Patterning

Try It

A

1. 17 ; 21 ; 25 ; 29
2. 7 ; 5 ; 3 ; 1
3. 17 ; 16 ; 19 ; 18
4. 7 ; 9 ; 6 ; 8
5. 8 ; 16 ; 12
    14 ; 11 ; 22
6. 13 ; 12 ; 15 ; 14
7. 30 ; 20 ; 25 ; 15 ; 20
8. 6 ; 12 ; 7 ; 14 ; 9
9. 7 ; 4 ; 6 ; 3 ; 5
10. 13 ; 16 ; 19
    1 ; 3
11. 10 ; 12 ; 13
    3 ; 1 ; 2
12. 17 ; 18 ; 13
    Start at 30. Subtract 5. Then add 1.
13. 18 ; 17 ; 34
    Start at 3. Multiply by 2. Then subtract 1.

14. 22 ; 44 ; 46
    Start at 2. Add 2. Then multiply by 2.
15. 9 ; 6 ; 5
16. 13 ; 26 ; 37
17. 5 ; 14 ; 42
18. 7 ; 57 ; 55
19a. A
  b. 9 ; 17 ; 34
20a. Start at 3. Multiply by 2. Then subtract 2.
  b. 12 ; 10 ; 18 ; 36
21a. 1 ; 3 ; 5 ; 7 ; 9
  b. Start at 1. Add 2 each time.
  c. 11 ; 15 ; 19
22a. 4 ; 7 ; 10 ; 13 ; 16
  b. Start at 4. Add 3 each time.
  c. 22 ; 28 ; 31

14 Simple Equations

Try It
15 ; 10
1. 4 + 8 = 12
   8 + 4 = 12
   12 − 4 = 8
   12 − 8 = 4
   8 ; 4
2. 3 x 5 = 15
   5 x 3 = 15
   15 ÷ 3 = 5
   15 ÷ 5 = 3
   3 ; 5
3. 4 x 5 = 20
   5 x 4 = 20
   20 ÷ 4 = 5
   20 ÷ 5 = 4
   5 ; 5
4. 6 + 7 = 13
   7 + 6 = 13
   13 − 6 = 7
   13 − 7 = 6
   13 ; 6
5. 3 ; 6
6. 48 ; 48
7. 15 − 7 = 8
   15 − 8 = 7
8. 3 + 13 = 16
   13 + 3 = 16
9. 45 ÷ 5 = 9
   45 ÷ 9 = 5

10. 7 x 9 = 63
    9 x 7 = 63
11. 4 + 17 = 21
    17 + 4 = 21
12. 4 x 7 = 28
    7 x 4 = 28
13. 21 ÷ 3 = 7
    21 ÷ 7 = 3
14. 3
15. 7
16. 12
17. 15
18. 3
19. 7
20. 16
21. 2
22. 4
23. 3
24. 13
25. 15
26. 1: ✗ ; 3
    2: ✔
    3: ✗ ; 20
    4: ✔
    5: ✗ ; 7
    6: ✔
    7: ✔
    8: ✔
    9: ✔
    10: ✔
    11: ✗ ; 10
    12: ✔
    13: ✔
    14: ✔
    10
27. 6
28. 21
29. 14
30. 32
31. 52
32. 49
33. 18
34. 5
35. 64
36. 4
37. 36
38. 2
39. 11
40. 7
    MATHEMATICS

Answers

15 Graphs

Try It
21 ; 21
1. 29 ; 31
2. 35 ; 35
3. 29 ; 46
4. 48 ; 48 and 51
5. D ; C ; A ; B
  a. C
  b. D
  c. C
  d. D
  e. A
  f. D
  g. B
  h. B
  i. B
  j. C
6. (Suggested answer)
It is easier to find the median and mode.
7a. hot dog
  b. 1 more
  c. 2 more
  d. 4 students
  e. 5 more
  f. 12 students
  g. 23 students
8. A
  a. 31
  b. 45 ; 46 years old
  c. 30 to 39 years old
  d. below 30 years old

16 Probability

Try It
4 ; 4 ; 4
1a. 3 ; 3 times
  b. 5 times ; 5 times
2a. 4 times ; 2 times
  b. 20 times ; 10 times
3a. 5 times ; 5 times
  b. 10 times ; 10 times
4a. 4 times ; 6 times
  b. 6 times ; 9 times
5a. 2 times ; 2 times
  b. 5 times ; 5 times
6a. 5 times ; 2 times
2 times ; 1 time

  b. 15 times ; 6 times
6 times ; 3 times
7a. Kate's Predictions
  b. 40 times ; 20 times ; 60 times
8. A
9. B
10. B
11.

+	1	2	3	4	5	6
1	2	3	4	5	6	7
2	3	4	5	6	7	8
3	4	5	6	7	8	9
4	5	6	7	8	9	10
5	6	7	8	9	10	11
6	7	8	9	10	11	12

  a. 2, 3, 4, 5, 6, 7, 8, 9, 10, 11, 12
  b. 3 ; 11
4 ; 10
5 ; 9
6 ; 8
7
  c. 2: 1
3: 2
4: 3
5: 4
6: 5
7: 6
8: 5
9: 4
10: 3
11: 2
12: 1
  d. Yes, he is correct. Exactly half of the 36 outcomes are even sums.

248 Complete MathSmart (Grade 4)

1 Addition and Subtraction

Try It
984 + 745 = 1729 ; 1729
1. 428 − 199 = 229 ; 229
2. 183 + 214 = 397 ; 397
3. 89 + 280 = 369 ; 369
4. 317 + 88 + 95 = 500 ; 500
5. 507 − 197 = 310 ; 310
6a. 3590 + 2945 = 6535 ; 6535
  b. 1782 + 2595 = 4377 ; 4377
  c. 2595 − 1782 = 813 ; 813
  d. 2945 − 1827 = 1118 ; 1118
  e. 3590 + 260 = 3850 ; 3850
  f. 1782 − 290 = 1492 ; 1492
7a. 876 + 1328 = 2204
   She biked 2204 m altogether.
  b. 686 + 1425 = 2111
   She biked 2111 m altogether.
  c. 1515 − 686 = 829
   She biked 829 m farther.
  d. 1372 − 876 = 496
   She biked 496 m farther.
  e. 1100 − 876 = 224
   She will have to bike 224 m farther.
  f. 829 + 1515 + 1372 = 3716
   She biked 3716 m altogether.
   876 + 1328 + 829 + 1515 + 1372 + 686 + 1425
   = 8031
   She biked 8031 m altogether.
8a. 1125 + 2540 = 3665
   There are 3665 seats altogether.
  b. 2540 − 970 = 1570
   There are 1570 more seats.
9a. 3411 + 2936 = 6347
   There are 6347 storybooks and picture
   books in the library.
  b. 3411 − 424 = 2987
   There are 2987 more storybooks.
10a. 692 + 299 = 991
   991 families have cats.
  b. 2579 − 991 = 1588
   1588 more families have dogs.

2 Multiplication and Division

Try It
30 x 6 = 180 ; 180
1. B ; 8 ; 8

$$\begin{array}{r} 8 \\ 3\overline{)2\ 4} \\ 2\ 4 \end{array}$$

2. A ; 64 ; 64

$$\begin{array}{r} 16 \\ \times\quad 4 \\ \hline 64 \end{array}$$

3. B ; 9 ; 9

$$\begin{array}{r} 2 \\ 9\overline{)1\ 8} \\ 1\ 8 \end{array}$$

4. 84 ÷ 7 ; 12 ; 12

$$\begin{array}{r} 1\ 2 \\ 7\overline{)8\ 4} \\ 7 \\ \hline 1\ 4 \\ 1\ 4 \end{array}$$

5. 96 ÷ 4 ; 24 ; 24

$$\begin{array}{r} 2\ 4 \\ 4\overline{)9\ 6} \\ 8 \\ \hline 1\ 6 \\ 1\ 6 \end{array}$$

6. 48 x 2 ; 96 ; 96

$$\begin{array}{r} 48 \\ \times\quad 2 \\ \hline 96 \end{array}$$

7. 32 x 3 ; 96 ; 96

$$\begin{array}{r} 32 \\ \times\quad 3 \\ \hline 96 \end{array}$$

8. 36 ÷ 3 ; 12 ; 12

$$\begin{array}{r} 1\ 2 \\ 3\overline{)3\ 6} \\ 3 \\ \hline 6 \\ 6 \end{array}$$

9. 5000 ÷ 100 = 50 ; 50
10. 12 x 10 = 120 ; 120
11. 2500 ÷ 100 = 25 ; 25
12. 20 x 1000 = 20 000 ; 20 000
13. 1500 ÷ 100 = 15 ; 15
14a. 97 ÷ 7 = 13R6
   There are 13 sandwiches in each bag.
  b. 6 sandwiches are left over.
15a. 29 ÷ 3 = 9R2
   There are 9 students in each group.
  b. 2 students are not in a group.
16. 12 x 8 = 96
   96 + 2 = 98
   There were 98 gumballs.

3   Mixed Operations with Whole Numbers

Try It

878 − 369 = 509 ; 509

1a. 26 x 5 = 130 ; 130

$$\begin{array}{r} 26 \\ \times\ \ 5 \\ \hline 130 \end{array}$$

b. 130 + 870 = 1000 ; 1000

$$\begin{array}{r} 130 \\ +\ \ 870 \\ \hline 1000 \end{array}$$

c. 1000 ÷ 100 = 10 ; 10

$$\begin{array}{r} 10 \\ 100\overline{)\ 1000} \\ \underline{1000} \end{array}$$

d. 1000 − 269 = 731 ; 731

$$\begin{array}{r} 1000 \\ -\ \ 269 \\ \hline 731 \end{array}$$

2a. 3108 − 1786 = 1322 ; 1322

b. 3108 + 1786 = 4894 ; 4894

3. 18 x 8 = 144 ; 144

4. $144 ÷ 6 = $24 ; 24

5. 12 x 4 = 48

48 ÷ 6 = 8

8

6. A: $\begin{array}{r} 1236 \\ +\ 2019 \\ \hline 3255 \end{array}$ B: $\begin{array}{r} 87 \\ \times\ \ \ 9 \\ \hline 783 \end{array}$

C: $\begin{array}{r} 2002 \\ -\ \ 182 \\ \hline 1820 \end{array}$ D: $\begin{array}{r} 3229 \\ -\ \ 978 \\ \hline 2251 \end{array}$

3255 ; 783 ; 1820 ; 2251

7a. 1236 + 1820 = 3056

Their total score is 3056 points.

b. 3255 + 1360 = 4615

Their total score is 4615 points.

8. 136 x 10 = 1360

It was Lily. She played Castle Quest.

9. 74 ÷ 4 = 18R2

There are 18 eggs in each carton. 2 eggs are left.

10. 36 x 7 = 252

She will have 252 cookies in all.

11. 9272 − 5593 = 3679

3679 saplings were left on the farm.

12. 20 ÷ 9 = 2R2

There are 2 stickers in the final row.

13. 38 ÷ 7 = 5R3

He can fill 5 dog bowls. 3 treats will be left.

14. 763 + 872 = 1635

1635 cherries were picked in all.

4   Fractions

Try It

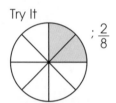

$; \frac{2}{8}$

1a.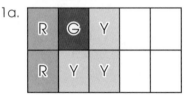

b. Ben: $\frac{2}{10}$; Jen: $\frac{1}{10}$; Tim: $\frac{3}{10}$

c. $\frac{6}{10}$ of the brownie was eaten.

d. $\frac{4}{10}$ of the brownie is left.

e. Ben and Tim ate $\frac{5}{10}$ of the brownie.

2.

He finished more of the assignment on Tuesday.

3.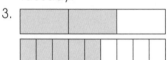

The apple pie had more of it eaten.

4.

a. He got the most work done on Tuesday.

b. He got the least work done on Wednesday.

c. Yes, he did.

5a. $\frac{3}{10}$ of them chose apples.

$\frac{2}{10}$ of them chose oranges.

b. $\frac{7}{10}$ of the class did not choose apples.

c. $\frac{4}{10}$ of them chose apples.

6a. $\frac{9}{10}$ of the Hawaiian pizza was eaten.

$\frac{6}{10}$ of the pepperoni pizza was eaten.

b. $\frac{3}{8}$ of the children ate 2 slices of Hawaiian pizza.

$\frac{2}{8}$ of the children ate 1 slice of pepperoni pizza.

7. Elsa had more cheesecake.

8. She ran more yesterday.

9. Meghan ate more pie.

10. Ashley was the tallest.

11. He will have read $\frac{7}{10}$ of the book after a week.

12. Jared's water bottle has more water.

5 Decimals

Try It

$2.1 - 1.6 = 0.5$; 0.5

1a. Keith is the tallest.

b. Judy is shorter than Keith but taller than Nicky.

c. $1.3 - 1.2 = 0.1$

$$\begin{array}{r} 1.3 \\ -\ 1.2 \\ \hline 0.1 \end{array}$$

Judy is 0.1 m taller.

d. $1.4 - 1.1 = 0.3$

$$\begin{array}{r} 1.4 \\ -\ 1.1 \\ \hline 0.3 \end{array}$$

The difference is 0.3 m.

2. $0.6 + 0.2 = 0.8$

He walked 0.8 km.

3. $0.8 - 0.5 = 0.3$

He would walk 0.3 km less.

4. $1.2 - 0.4 = 0.8$

Leo lives closer to Tom by 0.8 km.

5a. $0.6 + 0.4 = 1$

He walked 1 km.

b. $0.2 + 1.2 = 1.4$

He walked 1.4 km.

6. The boy is Tom.

7a. $1.3 + 2.5 = 3.8$

She swam 3.8 h in all.

b. $2.5 - 1.3 = 1.2$

She swam 1.2 h longer on Thursday.

8a. $1.5 + 1.4 + 1.6 = 4.5$

It took her 4.5 min.

b. $4.5 + 1.5 = 6$

It took her 6 min in total.

9. $1.5 + 1.7 + 1.7 = 4.9$

It took her 4.9 min.

10. $18 - 16.3 = 1.7$

Rich was faster by 1.7 s.

11. $2.4 + 1.7 = 4.1$

The weight of the watermelon is 4.1 kg.

12. 1 roll of blue ribbon: $2.5 - 0.6 = 1.9$

2 rolls of blue ribbon: $1.9 + 1.9 = 3.8$

The total length is 3.8 m.

13. Tree B: $4.2 + 0.7 = 4.9$

Tree C: $4.9 + 0.5 = 5.4$

Tree C is 5.4 m tall.

14. Afternoon: $6.7 + 3.3 = 10$

Evening: $10 - 2.5 = 7.5$

The temperature in the evening was 7.5°C.

15. $\$45.20 + \$4.90 = \$50.10$

Yes, she has enough money.

6 Money

Try It

$\$15 - \$11.35 = \$3.65$; 3.65

1a. $\$0.30 = 30¢ = 25¢ + 5¢$

He has a quarter and a nickel.

b. $30¢ - 20¢ = 10¢$

He will have 10¢ left.

2. $\$3.15 = \$2 + \$1 + 10¢ + 5¢$

She used a toonie, a loonie, a dime, and a nickel.

3. 4 quarters = $1 ; 12 quarters = $3

$\$5.50 - \$3 = \$2.50$

$\$2.50 = 250¢ = 25 \times 10¢ = 25$ dimes

She has 25 dimes.

4. $\$16.25 + \$5.80 = \$22.05$

He has $22.05 now.

$$\begin{array}{r} 16.25 \\ +\ 5.80 \\ \hline 22.05 \end{array}$$

5a. $\$1.60 + \$1.60 = \$3.20$

The total cost was $3.20.

$$\begin{array}{r} 1.60 \\ +\ 1.60 \\ \hline 3.20 \end{array}$$

b. $\$5 - \$3.20 = \$1.80$

Her change was $1.80.

$$\begin{array}{r} 5.00 \\ -\ 3.20 \\ \hline 1.80 \end{array}$$

6a. $\$50.20 - \$36.75 = \$13.45$

He has $13.45 more.

$$\begin{array}{r} 50.20 \\ -36.75 \\ \hline 13.45 \end{array}$$

b. $\$50.20 + \$36.75 = \$86.95$

No, they cannot afford it.

$$\begin{array}{r} 50.20 \\ +36.75 \\ \hline 86.95 \end{array}$$

7a. $\$4.49 + \$2.50 = \$6.99$

It costs $6.99.

b. $\$11.90 + \$2.15 = \$14.05$

It costs $14.05.

8. $\$2.35 + \$2.15 = \$4.50$

She needs $4.50.

9. $20 – $11.90 = $8.10
    His change was $8.10.
10. 2 toonies = $4
    $4.49 – $4 = $0.49
    She needs $0.49 more.
11. Three $5 bills = $15
    $15 – $11.90 = $3.10
    His change was $3.10.
12a. Total: $15.75 + $3.85 = $19.60
    Change: $20 – $19.60 = $0.40
    Her change was $0.40.
    Joan's change:

b. Total: $24.50 + $15.75 = $40.25
    Change: $50 – $40.25 = $9.75
    His change was $9.75.
    Alan's change:

c. Total: $0.50 + $21.40 = $21.90
    Change: $25 – $21.90 = $3.10
    Her change was $3.10.
    Katie's change:

7 Perimeter and Area

Try It
area
1. perimeter
2. area
3. perimeter
4. area
5. area
6.

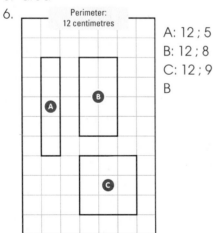

A: 12 ; 5
B: 12 ; 8
C: 12 ; 9
B

7.

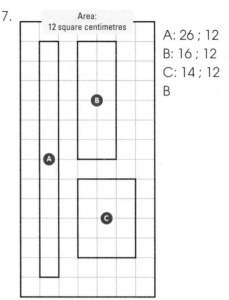

A: 26 ; 12
B: 16 ; 12
C: 14 ; 12
B

8. area
    16 × 9 = 144
    The window is 144 square decimetres.

    16 dm
    9 dm

9. perimeter
    16 + 9 + 16 + 9 = 50
    50 m of fencing is needed.

    16 m
    9 m

10. area
    4 × 2 = 8
    The rug covers 8 square metres.

    4 m
    2 m

11. perimeter
    3 + 3 + 3 + 3 = 12
    She needs 12 m of frill material.

    3 m
    3 m

12. perimeter
    15 + 20 + 15 + 20 = 70
    He needs 70 cm of wood.

    15 cm
    20 cm

13. 20 + 30 + 20 + 30 = 100 (cm) = 1 (m)
    2 – 1 = 1
    Yes, the wooden strip is long enough to frame the poster. 1 m of wooden strip will be left over.
14. 50 × 50 = 2500
    The bulletin board is 2500 square centimetres.
15a. Square quilt: 20 × 20 = 400
    100 cm = 10 dm
    Rectangular quilt: 8 × 10 = 80
    The square quilt is larger.
  b. Square quilt: 20 + 20 + 20 + 20 = 80
    100 cm = 10 dm
    Rectangular quilt: 8 + 10 + 8 + 10 = 36
    Difference: 80 – 36 = 44
    The square quilt needs 44 dm more frills.

16. Area of 1 plank: 100 x 10 = 1000 (square
    centimetres)
    Area of patio: 200 x 600 = 120 000 (square
    centimetres)
    Number of planks: 120 000 ÷ 1000 = 120
    He needs 120 planks.

8 Mass, Capacity, and Volume

Try It
kg ; L ; mg ; mL
1. 400 g
2. cornflakes
3. sausages
4. salt
5. cornflakes
6. 250 g
7. potatoes, sausages, bananas, cornflakes,
   salt
8. 4
9. 2
10. 3
11. 3
12. 6
13. 4
14. mug, bottle of syrup, bottle of soap, carton
    of milk, bucket
15a. Structure A
  b. Structure C
  c. 11 x 1 x 1
16a. capacity ; 500 mL x 3 = 1500 mL
    The 3 bottles can hold 1500 mL.
  b. mass ; 350 g x 3 = 1050 g
    The 3 bottles weigh 1050 g.
17a. A ; volume ; 3 x 1 x 6 = 18
    It takes up 18 cubic centimetres.
  b. mass ; 250 g x 2 = 500 g
    The 2 towers weigh 500 g in total.
18. volume ; 2 x 2 x 2 = 8

    The cube takes up 8 cubic centimetres.
19. 1000 g ÷ 200 g = 5
    She needs to buy 5 bags of flour.

20. 4000 mL ÷ 500 mL = 8
    She needs 8 cartons of milk.
21. 5 g x 2 = 10 g = 10 000 mg
    He added 10 000 mg of sugar.
22a. 200 g x 4 = 800 g
    The total mass of the bowls is 800 g.
  b. 8 L x 4 = 32 L
    The bowls can hold 32 L of fruit punch.
23. 50 – 18 = 32
    The big tower takes up 32 cubic centimetres
    more space.

9 Shapes and Solids

Try It
7
1. There are 4 quadrilaterals.
2a. The square, trapezoid, rectangle, and
    parallelogram have parallel sides.
  b. The square and rectangle have right
    angles.
  c. The square has 4 lines of symmetry.
3.

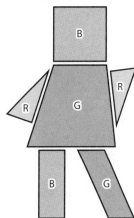

4a. 7 quadrilaterals
  b. 4 shapes
  c. Max: Ali:
     rhombus   parallelogram
  d. Kyle said this.

     The shape is a trapezoid.
  e. ◁▷ or ⬦⬦
     He could get 2 triangles or 2 parallelograms.
5. prism

6-9. (Suggested drawings)

6.

It is a square-based pyramid.

7a.

It is a cube.

b.

It is a rectangular prism.

8a.
 or
The solid could be a rectangular prism or a hexagonal pyramid.

b.

The solid is a hexagonal pyramid.

9a.

It is a hexagonal pyramid.

b.

It is a pentagonal prism.

10. Net A can be folded into a solid. It is a cube.

11. She can make a triangular prism or a pentagonal pyramid.

12. He needs 1 more ball of clay and 3 more sticks.

10   Grid Maps

Try It
B1, C4, and E3

1a. B5, F3, and H2

b. B2, C3, and H5

c. A5, E4, and I2

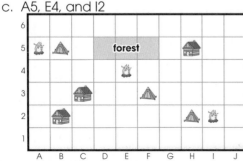

2a. The closest campfire spot is at E4.

b. They should go 1 block up and 2 blocks to the right.

3a. The tent is at H2.

b. Her friend should go 1 block up and 5 blocks to the left.

4.
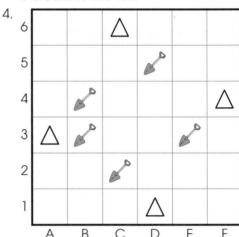

5. The coordinates are B3, B4, C2, D5, and E3.

6. They need to be careful when digging at B3 and B4.

7a. Swings: D14, D15, E14, E15, F14, F15, G14, and G15
Monkey bars: B8, B9, C8, C9, D8, and D9
Sea-saw: D4, E4, and F4
Slide: B18, B19, B20, C18, C19, C20, D18, D19, and D20

b. He went to the swings.

c. She went to the monkey bars.

8. The coordinates are E2, G6, and L4 respectively.

9a. He should sail 4 blocks to the right and 2 blocks down.

b. He should sail 2 blocks to the right and 4 blocks up.

c. He should sail 5 blocks to the right and 2 blocks down.

10. Leo sits beside Liza.

11. Jane sits in the same row as Anne.

11   Patterning

Try It
10 ; 12 ; 12

1a. 7 ; 9 ; 11 ; 13 ; 15 ; 17 ; 19

b. He bought 13 marbles in Week 5.

c. He bought 17 marbles in Week 7.

d. 5 + 7 + 9 + 11 + 13 + 15 = 60
He bought 60 marbles in all.

e. He will buy 23 marbles in Week 10.

2a. 9 ; 8 ; 7 ; 6

b. There are 7 blocks in Layer 4.

c. 10 + 9 + 8 = 27
There are 3 layers.

d. 10 + 9 + 8 + 7 + 6 = 40
There are 40 blocks in 5 layers.

3a. 20 ; 25 ; 30 ; 35 ; 40

b. Lap 4 took him 30 s to finish.

c. It took him 40 s to finish the final lap.

d. 15 + 20 + 25 + 30 + 35 + 40 = 165
It took him 165 s to complete the race.

4a.

1	2	3	4	5	6
10	20	30	40	50	60

b. 40 crayons have been given out by Week 4.

c. 100 – 60 = 40
She has 40 crayons left by the end of Week 6.

d. The last batch of the crayons will be given out in Week 10.

5a.

Jan	Feb	Mar	Apr	May	Jun
128	64	32	16	8	4

b. There were 8 candies left in May.

c. 128 – 16 = 112
112 candies in total were eaten.

6.

Week	1	2	3	4	5	6	7
Cent	5	10	15	20	25	30	35

She will have 35¢.

7.

Day	1	2	3	4	5	6	7	8
No. of Stickers	7	11	15	19	23	27	31	35

He will have 35 stickers.

8a.

Day	Mon	Tue	Wed	Thu	Fri	Sat
No. of Worksheets	3	5	7	9	11	13

She will complete 11 worksheets on Friday.

b. She will complete 13 worksheets on Saturday.

9a.

Day	Mon	Tue	Wed	Thu	Fri
No. of Pies	7	10	13	16	19

She will bake 19 pies.

b.

Day	Mon	Tue	Wed	Thu	Fri	Sat	Sun
No. of Cakes	12	10	8	6	4	2	0

She will bake 0 cakes.

12 Equations

Try It
A ; 4

1. A
She hid 6 marbles.

2. B
9 marbles rolled away.

3. A
She had 8 red marbles to start with.

4. B
He started with 14 peanuts.

5. A
David had 9 cards to start with.

6. B
He bought 6 boxes of cookies.

7. A
She baked 3 trays of muffins.

8. A
There are 16 rows.

9a. 3 + ? = 15
He needs 12 more pencils.

b. 15 – ? = 3
She gave away 12 lollipops.

c. ? – 3 = 15
18 apples were in the basket.

d. 15 ÷ ? = 3
She needs 5 boxes.

e. ? ÷ 3 = 15
There are 45 roses in the bouquet.

10a. 30 ÷ ? = 6
There are 5 hats in each stack.

b. 6 x ? = 30
5 bags are needed.

c. ? – 5 = 6
There are 11 chapters.

d. ? ÷ 6 = 5
She has 30 blocks in all.

e. ? + 6 = 30
He has 24 blocks.

13 Graphs

Try It
Juice

1. Milk is the least popular.

2. 3 more boys than girls voted for juice.

3. 3 more girls voted for juice than milk.

4. 7 students chose juice over pop.

5. 3 students chose pop over milk.

6.

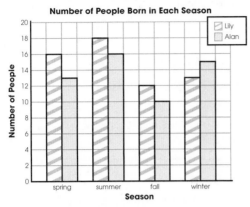

Number of People Born in Each Season

a. Summer has the most birthdays.

b. 6 more of Lily's friends were born in summer than fall.

c. 2 more of Lily's friends than Alan's were born in fall.

d. Lily: 16 + 18 + 12 + 13 = 59
   Alan: 13 + 16 + 10 + 15 = 54
   59 – 54 = 5
   Lily surveyed 5 more people.

7. Munchball

Stem	Leaf
0	2 5 6 7
1	0 2 3 8 8 9 9
2	0 0 0 2 2 4 5 7 7 8 8
3	2 5 7

Spacekins

Stem	Leaf
0	1 4 6 7
1	0 2 4 5 5 9
2	4 5 5 7 9
3	0 0 1 1 3 4 5 6 7 9

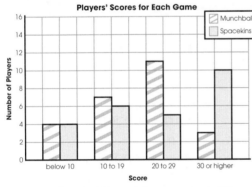

Players' Scores for Each Game

8a. The median is 20 and the mode is 20.

b. The median is 25 and the modes are 15, 25, 30, and 31.

9a. 37 – 2 = 35 ; The range is 35.

b. 39 – 1 = 38 ; The range is 38.

10. There were 4 fewer players.

11. She is talking about Munchball.

12. She should play Spacekins.

14 Probability

Try It

$\frac{1}{2}$

1.

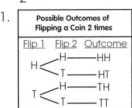

Possible Outcomes of Flipping a Coin 2 times

Prediction: 5 ; 5 times ; 5 times ; 5 times
Result: (Individual results)

2. Yes, the more times you repeat the experiment, the closer the results will be to the predictions.

3a. He will get heads about 5 times.

b. He will get tails about 25 times.

4a. Set B is William's because there are 2 "1" out of 5.

b. Set C is Oliver's because there are 3 "2" out of 5.

5a. He will get an "A" about 5 times.

b. He removes a "B" ball.

6.

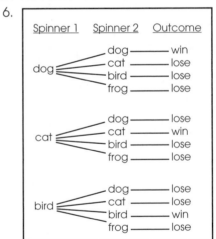

7. The probability is $\frac{3}{12}$.

8. The probability is $\frac{9}{12}$.

9. The player will get a prize about 15 times.

10. The predicted outcome is that no player will win a prize 3 times out of 4. If the game is played 120 times, there will be about 90 times when no one wins the game. So it is reasonable.

ASSESSMENT TESTS 1 AND 2

Test-taking Tips

Writing tests can be stressful for many students. The best way to prepare for a test is by practising! In addition to practising, the test-taking tips below will also help you prepare for tests.

Multiple-choice Questions

- Read the question twice before finding the answer.
- Skip the difficult questions and do the easy ones first.
- Come up with an answer before looking at the choices.
- Read all four choices before deciding which is the correct answer.
- Eliminate the choices that you know are incorrect.
- Read and follow the instructions carefully:
  - Use a pencil only.
  - Fill one circle only for each question.
  - Fill the circle completely.
  - Cleanly erase any answer you wish to change.
    e.g.

    correct   incorrect

Open-response Questions

- Read the question carefully.
- Highlight (i.e. underline/circle) important information in the question.
- Use drawings to help you better understand the question if needed.
- Find out what needs to be included in the solution.
- Estimate the answer.
- Organize your thoughts before writing the solution.
- Write in the space provided.
- Always write a concluding sentence for your solution.
- Check if your answer is reasonable.
- Never leave a question blank. Show your work or write down your reasoning. Even if you do not get the correct answer, you might get some marks for showing your work.

Multiple-choice Questions

You may not use a calculator or manipulatives for Questions 1 – 4.

① What are the sum and difference of 3419 and 4207?

○ sum: 7616; difference: 798

○ sum: 7689; difference: 1212

○ sum: 7626; difference: 788

○ sum: 7725; difference: 812

② What is the answer?

4 – 2.7 = ?

○ 0.7

○ 1.3

○ 2.7

○ 3.3

③ Which division problem has a remainder of 2?

○ 89 ÷ 4

○ 68 ÷ 5

○ 90 ÷ 6

○ 51 ÷ 7

④ What are the values of ●, ■, and ▲?

33 x ● = 33
■ ÷ 5 = ■
▲ ÷ 1 = 1

○ ● = 0 ■ = 0 ▲ = 1

○ ● = 0 ■ = 1 ▲ = 0

○ ● = 1 ■ = 0 ▲ = 0

○ ● = 1 ■ = 0 ▲ = 1

You may now use a calculator and/or manipulatives.

⑤ Which fraction describes the shaded part of the set?

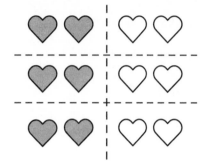

- ○ $\frac{2}{3}$
- ○ $\frac{3}{6}$
- ○ $\frac{3}{4}$
- ○ $\frac{3}{12}$

⑥ Which equation has the greatest missing number?

- ○ ⬚ x 10 = 400
- ○ 5 x ⬚ = 5000
- ○ ⬚ x 20 = 200
- ○ 300 x ⬚ = 3000

⑦ Which of the decimals is equivalent to $2\frac{3}{5}$?

- ○ 2.3
- ○ 2.5
- ○ 2.6
- ○ 2.8

⑧ The total cost of the two toys below is greater than $22.

What is the cost of the stuffed bear?

- ○ $8.45
- ○ $9
- ○ $9.05
- ○ $9.45

⑨ What is the perimeter of the shape?

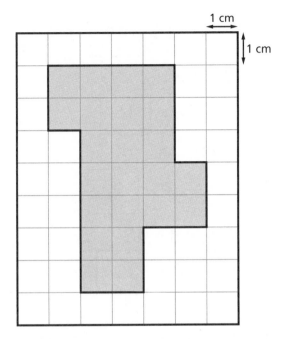

1 cm

1 cm

○ 22 cm

○ 23 cm

○ 24 cm

○ 25 cm

⑩ Which conversion is incorrect?

○ 4 m = 400 mm

○ 7 dm = 70 cm

○ 20 L = 20 000 mL

○ 8000 mg = 8 g

⑪ What solid does the net form?

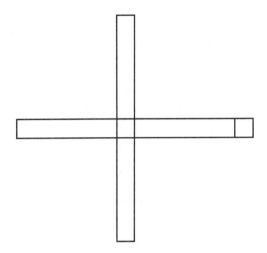

○ square-based pyramid

○ rectangular pyramid

○ triangular prism

○ rectangular prism

⑫ What is the pattern rule?

8, 6, 12, 10, 20, 18

○ Start at 8. Add 2. Then subtract 6.

○ Start at 8. Subtract 2. Then multiply by 2.

○ Start at 8. Multiply by 2. Then subtract 2.

○ Start at 8. Subtract 2. Then add 6.

⑬ Which of the following is not a reflection?

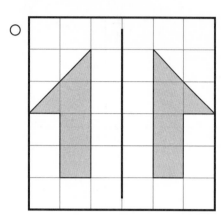

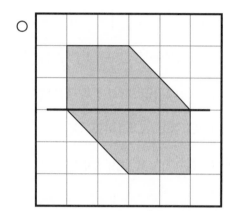

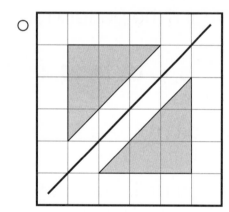

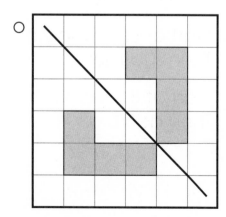

⑭ Which solution is correct?

○ 23 + L = 45

L = | 12 |

○ S ÷ 8 = 2

S = | 16 |

○ 50 – P = 38

P = | 22 |

○ A × 8 = 45

A = | 5 |

⑮ What are the median and mode?

46	30	42	24	24
47	34	39	51	57
47	42	66	47	79

○ median: 46;
   mode: 47

○ median: 46;
   mode: 24, 42, and 47

○ median: 47;
   mode: 46

○ median: 47;
   mode: 42 and 47

Open-response Questions

⑯ The locations of street lights are listed below. Draw ⌐ on the grid map at the given coordinates.

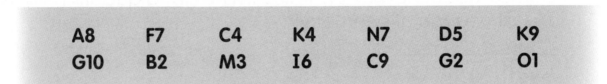

A8	F7	C4	K4	N7	D5	K9
G10	B2	M3	I6	C9	G2	O1

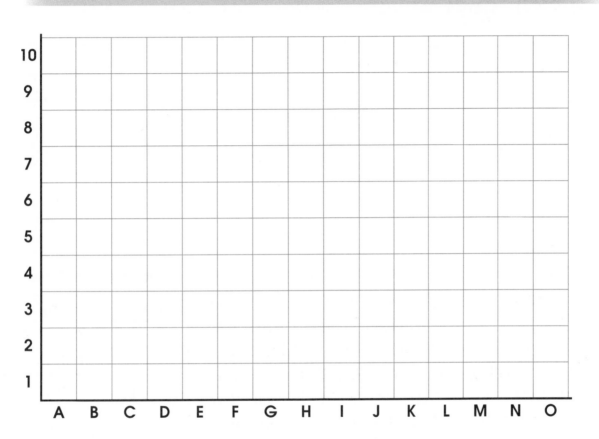

Four of the street lights are at the corners of a rectangular park. Write the coordinates of these 4 street lights. What is the area of the park?

⑰ Henry has six cards, each showing a quadrilateral as shown. He shuffles them and draws one card at random. If he does this 30 times, about how many times will he get a quadrilateral with at least one line of symmetry?

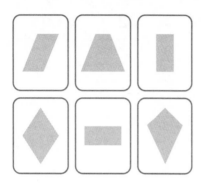

⑱ Each card in a 30-card deck has a number on it. Abby and Belle split the cards and recorded their numbers using stem-and-leaf plots. What are the median and mode for the entire deck? If a "15" is added, will the median for the entire deck change? If so, what will the new median be?

Abby's 15 Cards

Stem	Leaf
0	2 3 4 7 8
1	1 1 2
2	2 2 6
3	0 5 7 7

Belle's 15 Cards

Stem	Leaf
0	1 8 9
1	0 1 2 3 5
2	2 3 6 6 7
3	6 8

Multiple-choice Questions

> **You may not use a calculator or manipulatives for Questions 1 – 4.**

① Which of the following addition or subtraction sentences is incorrect?

- ○ 2375 + 4295 = 6670
- ○ 3682 – 2247 = 1445
- ○ 6500 – 1988 = 4512
- ○ 5033 + 4126 = 9159

② Which multiplication problem has the greatest product?

- ○ 65 x 7
- ○ 46 x 8
- ○ 35 x 9
- ○ 92 x 5

③ What is the answer?

$$\begin{array}{r} 1.8 \\ +\quad 0.5 \\ \hline \end{array}$$

- ○ 1.5
- ○ 2.3
- ○ 2.5
- ○ 2.8

④ Which long division is correct?

○
$$\begin{array}{r} 20 \\ 4\overline{)83} \\ 8 \\ \hline 3 \\ 0 \\ \hline \end{array}$$

○
$$\begin{array}{r} 21\,R2 \\ 3\overline{)65} \\ 6 \\ \hline 5 \\ 3 \\ \hline 2 \end{array}$$

○
$$\begin{array}{r} 13 \\ 6\overline{)78} \\ 18 \\ \hline 60 \\ 60 \\ \hline \end{array}$$

○
$$\begin{array}{r} 11\,R3 \\ 7\overline{)90} \\ 7 \\ \hline 10 \\ 7 \\ \hline \end{array}$$

You may now use a calculator and/or manipulatives.

⑤ Which fraction is the greatest?

○ $\frac{2}{4}$

○ $\frac{3}{4}$

○ $\frac{1}{2}$

○ $\frac{1}{4}$

⑥ What is the missing part of the equation?

$$1200 \boxed{} = 12$$

○ x 10

○ x 100

○ ÷ 10

○ ÷ 100

⑦ Which fraction is equal to 1.8?

○ $\frac{8}{10}$

○ $1\frac{3}{5}$

○ $1\frac{4}{5}$

○ $1\frac{1}{8}$

⑧ How much money is there?

○ $44.70

○ $50.45

○ $52.75

○ $54.80

⑨ What is the area of the rectangle?

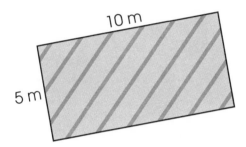

10 m

5 m

○ 15 square metres

○ 25 square metres

○ 30 square metres

○ 50 square metres

⑩ Look at the measurements of the containers below.

Vase
1 kg
1500 mL
20 cubic centimetres

Jug
3 L
50 cubic centimetres
500 g

Which statement is correct?

○ A vase can balance 2 jugs on a scale.

○ The vase has a greater volume than the jug.

○ 2 jugs can fill up a vase.

○ The vase has a greater capacity than the jug.

⑪ What is the elapsed time?

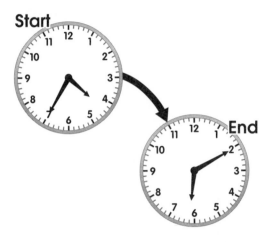

Start

End

○ 0 hours 55 minutes

○ 1 hour 10 minutes

○ 1 hour 35 minutes

○ 2 hours 5 minutes

⑫ If the spinner is spun 40 times, about how many times will it land on C?

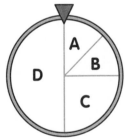

○ 5 times

○ 10 times

○ 15 times

○ 20 times

⑬ Which of the following is the correct way for Jon to reach the given item?

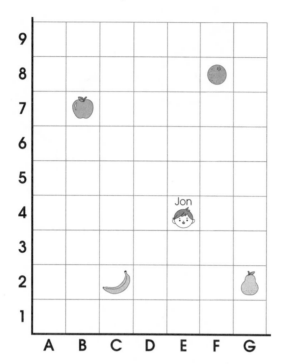

- ○ 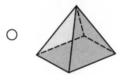: Move 4 blocks up and 3 blocks to the left.

- ○ 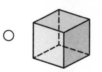: Move 4 blocks up and 1 block to the left.

- ○ : Move 2 blocks to the left and 2 blocks up.

- ○ : Move 2 blocks to the right and 2 blocks down.

⑭ Which solid has 6 faces, 6 vertices, and 10 edges?

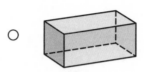

○

○

○

⑮ Which quadrilateral never has right angles?

- ○ trapezoid
- ○ rectangle
- ○ parallelogram
- ○ kite

⑯ Liz and Ben opened their piggy banks and recorded their coins in the double bar graph, but they each missed one bar.

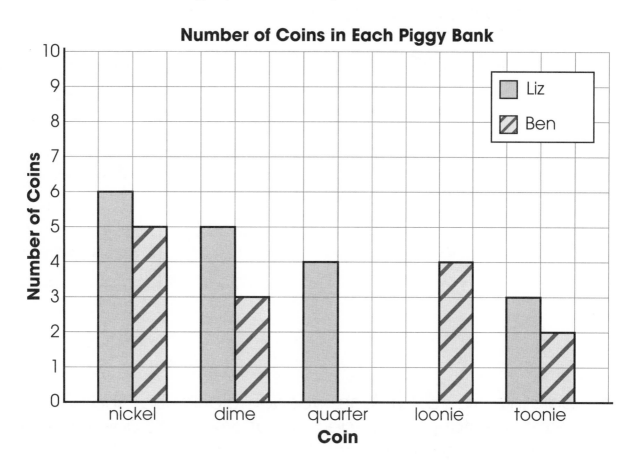

Number of Coins in Each Piggy Bank

Each child has a total of 20 coins. Help Liz and Ben complete the bar graph. Who has more money?

⑰ Nicole enjoys collecting marbles. On Saturday, June 1, she had 4 marbles. Then on every Saturday after, she added 3 marbles to her collection. On what date did she have 31 marbles?

June						
S	M	T	W	TH	F	S
						1
2	3	4	5	6	7	8
9	10	11	12	13	14	15
16	17	18	19	20	21	22
23	24	25	26	27	28	29
30						

July						
S	M	T	W	TH	F	S
	1	2	3	4	5	6
7	8	9	10	11	12	13
14	15	16	17	18	19	20
21	22	23	24	25	26	27
28	29	30	31			

⑱ Caroline has 16 1-m-long wooden planks that she will use to make a rectangular garden. What are the possible dimensions of the rectangular gardens she can make? Which one has the greatest area?

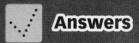

Assessment Test 1

1. sum: 7626; difference: 788
2. 1.3
3. 51 ÷ 7
4. ◯ = 1 ▇ = 0 △ = 1
5. $\frac{3}{6}$
6. 5 x ▭ = 5000
7. 2.6
8. $9.45
9. 24 cm
10. 4 m = 400 mm
11. rectangular prism
12. Start at 8. Subtract 2. Then multiply by 2.
13.

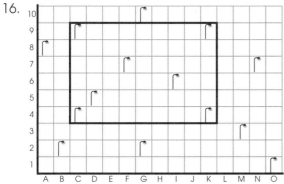

14. S ÷ 8 = 2

    S = ▭ 16

15. median: 46;
    mode: 47
16.

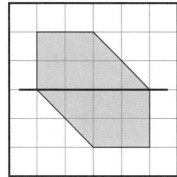

The street lights are at C4, C9, K4, and K9.
Area of the park: 9 x 6 = 54
The area of the park is 54 square units.

17. 5 out of 6 quadrilaterals have at least one line of symmetry.
    He would get a quadrilateral with at least one line of symmetry about 25 times.

18.

Entire Deck

Stem	Leaf
0	1 2 3 4 7 8 8 9
1	0 1 1 1 2 2 ③ ⑤ ── (13 + 15) ÷ 2 = 14
2	2 2 2 3 6 6 6 7
3	0 5 6 7 7 8

The median is 14. The modes are 11, 22, and 26.

Entire Deck + "15"

Stem	Leaf
0	1 2 3 4 7 8 8 9
1	0 1 1 1 2 2 3 ⑤ 5
2	2 2 2 3 6 6 6 7
3	0 5 6 7 7 8

Yes, the median for the entire deck will change. The new median will be 15.

Assessment Test 2

1. 3682 – 2247 = 1445
2. 92 x 5
3. 2.3
4.
```
    2 1 R2
  3⟌6 5
    6
    ‾
      5
      3
      ‾
      2
```
5. $\frac{3}{4}$
6. ÷ 100
7. $1\frac{4}{5}$
8. $54.80
9. 50 square metres
10. A vase can balance 2 jugs on a scale.
11. 1 hour 35 minutes
12. 10 times
13. 🍐 : Move 2 blocks to the right and 2 blocks down.
14.

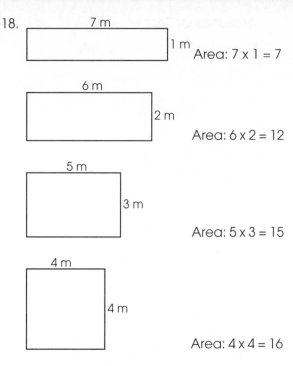

15. parallelogram
16.

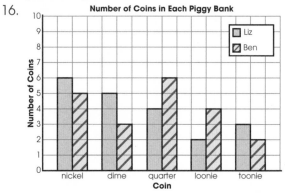

Liz has $9.80 and Ben has $10.05. Ben has more money.

17.
Jun 1 Jun 8 Jun 15 Jun 22 Jun 29 Jul 6 Jul 13 Jul 20 Jul 27 Aug 3
  4   7   10   13   16   19   22   25   28   31

She had 31 marbles on Saturday, August 3.

18.

Area: 7 x 1 = 7

Area: 6 x 2 = 12

Area: 5 x 3 = 15

Area: 4 x 4 = 16

The possible dimensions are 7 m by 1 m, 6 m by 2 m, 5 m by 3 m, and 4 m by 4 m. The one that is 4 m by 4 m has the greatest area.